The
Host

C000218491

England
Wales
Scotland

Edited by

Sam Dalley and Penny MacGregor

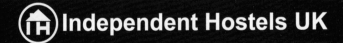
Independent Hostels UK

ISBN 978-1-7398832-1-8

Independent Hostel Guide 2023: England, Wales & Scotland. 31st Edition.

Editors: Sam Dalley and Penny MacGregor.
Photo Editor: Toby Bumby

British Library Cataloguing in Publication Data. A catalogue record for this book is available at the British Library **ISBN 978-1-7398832-1-8**

Published by: Independent Hostels UK, Speedwell House, Upperwood, Matlock Bath, Derbyshire, DE4 3PE.
Tel: +44 (0) 1629 580427.

© Independent Hostels UK, 2023

Printed by: Zenith zenithprint.co.uk

Cover Artwork: Bronia Kidd **Cover Photos:** Front Cover photo: Lewis Dodds. Back cover (top to bottom), Kingshouse Bunkhouse pg 155a, Isle of Muck Bunkhouse pg169b, Igloo Hybrid pg 44b.

Internal Photographs: Photo on page 175 credited to Brian Sutherland. Photo on page 178 credited to Ike Gibson. Photo on page 134 credited to Mike Emmett. Photo on page 129 credited to Mick Garratt. Photos on page 85 credited to Elliott Simpson. Photos on page 172 credited to Visit Scotland/Paul Tomkins. Photos on page 160 credited to Allan Sutherland, Paul Higson, Colin McLean and Tom Daly. **Other photos were supplied by the accommodation featured. All copyright is retained.**

Visit our booking platform. Awarded Best Buy. *Ethical Consumer, 2022*

ISBN 9781739883218

9 781739 883218

Distributed in the UK by:
Cordee Ltd
Unit 11 Dodwells Bridge Industrial Estate
Hinckley, Leicestershire
LE10 3BS. Tel : 01455 611 185

CONTENTS

INDEPENDENT HOSTELS UK

Independent Hostels UK is a network of over 320 bunkhouses, hostels, camping barns and group accommodation centres. These provide a unique form of accommodation, ideal for groups, individuals and families who enjoy good company, independent travel and the great outdoors.

Independenthostels.co.uk

WHAT ARE
INDEPENDENT HOSTELS?

Friendly places to stay

Shared kitchens and lounges

Private bedrooms and bunks

Perfect for short stays

Families, individuals and groups all welcome

No membership needed

In some amazing locations

Great value

At the forefront of sustainable tourism

Wooler Youth Hostel pg 99b

The start of your next adventure

SYMBOLS

	Dormitories
	Private rooms (often ideal for families)
	Sleeping bags required
	Hostel fully heated
	Some areas heated
	Drying room available
	Cooking facilities available
	Meals provided or available locally
	WiFi available
	Simple accommodation: basic, clean and friendly
	Dogs welcome by prior arrangement
	Bike shed
	Bronze, Silver, Gold, Green Tourism Award
	Affiliated to Hostelling International
	Accommodation for groups only
pp	per person
	Some accessible areas (See Index pages 189-192)

Follow our social media for special offers

     @indiehostelsuk

WELCOME TO
THE WORLD OF INDEPENDENT HOSTELS

This guide and our booking platform open the door to the largest network of hostels and bunkhouses in the UK.

Where you can talk to your hosts and place your booking direct, at the lowest possible prices.

Visit our booking platform now:
Independenthostels.co.uk

INDEPENDENT HOSTELS UK DECLARES
A CLIMATE EMERGENCY

We pledge to:

REDUCE - our carbon footprint (slimmer guidebook)

PROMOTE - eco hostels and green travel

ENCOURAGE - hostels to improve their eco credentials

www.tourismdeclares.com

AWARDED BEST BUY
BY ETHICAL CONSUMER

In summer 2022 Ethical Consumer ranked Independent Hostels UK as the third most ethical holiday booking company out of 29 brands.

"Only three companies on our table, Independent Hostels, FairBnB and Canopy & Stars, all small companies offering environmental alternatives, scored our best rating for carbon management. All were tackling their own operational impacts and working with their accommodation providers to reduce their emissions too." **Ethical Consumer, July 2022**

The Guardian Newspaper sang our praises in an article which denounced the poor ethical and carbon reduction policies of the big booking sites.

"Independent Hostels UK, which collates independently owned hostels across the UK into one online guide, were recommended alongside Canopy & Stars and Fairbnb as the sites that consumers should book with for ethical practices." **The Guardian, Summer 2022**

www.ethicalconsumer.org

DRYING ROOMS

Many hostels and bunkhouses have drying rooms.

You can go out in all weathers, confident of a dry start the next day.

Look out for this symbol

Bike store at Radcliffes Lodge 98a

Drying room at Saddle Mountain Hostel 163a

BIKE SHEDS

Many bunkhouses and hostels have sheds for storing your cycles and equipment.

Look out for this symbol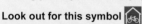

On our website the extra symbol 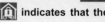 indicates that the shed is secure.

Don't let the weather stop you

PRIVATE ROOMS

Family room at Ocean Backpackers pg 23a

Many hostels have private rooms.

Some small for couples.

Others larger for families.

Many are en suite.

Look out for this symbol and on our website you can also see when these are ideal for families

Privacy at night, social in the daytime

ACCOMMODATION ON
LONG DISTANCE ROUTES

Independenthostels.co.uk/trails

If you are planning a long distance route this year be sure to check our website.

We map 50 of the most popular walking, pilgrimage and cycling routes, with details of hostels along the way.

Geared up for walkers and cyclists they usually offer:

Single night stop-overs

Breakfast & packed-lunches

Drying rooms and secure bike storage

Hot showers and comfy lounges

DOG FRIENDLY

Over a third of hostels and bunkhouses welcome dogs.

Please be sure to mention your dog when you book. There may be a small extra fee.

Don't leave your faithful friend behind again

Look out for this symbol:-

Independenthostels.co.uk/dog

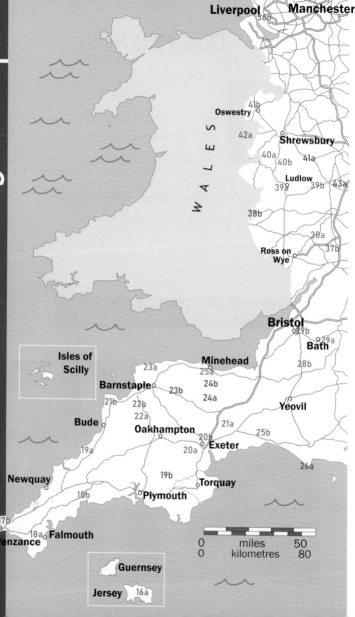

South England

Liverpool   Manchester

56b

Oswestry 41b

42a

Shrewsbury

40a 40b 41a

Ludlow

39a 39b 43a

38b

38a

37b

Ross on
Wye

Bristol

49b 29a

Bath

28b

Isles of
Scilly

Minehead

23a 25a

24b

Barnstaple 23b 24a

Yeovil

21b 22b

22a

Bude Oakhampton 21a

25b

20b

20a Exeter

19a

26a

Newquay

19b

Torquay

18b Plymouth

17b

17a

16b 18a Falmouth

Penzance

0   miles   50
0   kilometres   80

Guernsey

Jersey 16a

South England

KEY

45 - **Page number**

45a - **Left side of page**

45b - **Right side of page**

45 - **Groups only**

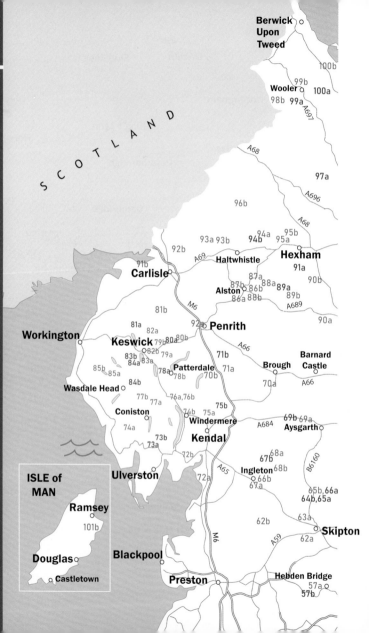

Berwick Upon Tweed

100b

Wooler 99b 100a
98b 99a A697

A68

97a

A696

A68

96b

93a 93b 94a 94b 95b
92b A69 Haltwhistle 94b 95a Hexham
91b Carlisle 87a 88a 89a 91a
Alston 87b 86b 89b 90b
86a 88b A689
81b M6 90a
81a 82a 92a Penrith
Keswick 79b 80a 80b
82b 79a 71b A66 Barnard
83b 85a 83a Brough Castle
85b 84a 83a 84b 70a A66
Wasdale Head 84b 70b
77b 77a 78a Patterdale 71a
Coniston 76a,76b 75b
74a 73b 75a A684 69b 69a
73a Windermere Aysgarth
72b Kendal 68a
Ulverston 72a A65 67b
Ingleton 68b
66b 65b,66a
67a 64b,65a
62b 63a
62a Skipton
A59

ISLE of MAN

Ramsey
101b

Douglas
Castletown

Blackpool

M6

Preston

Hebden Bridge
57a
57b

Workington

SCOTLAND

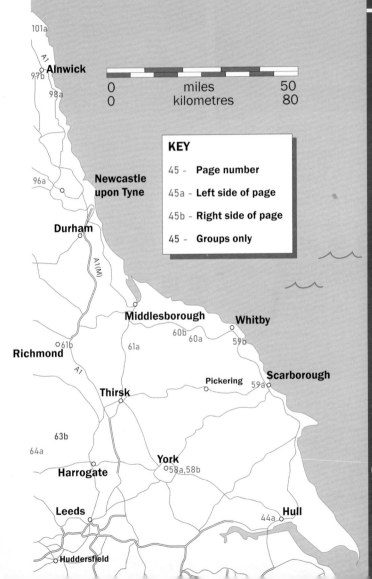

North England

0   miles   50
0   kilometres   80

KEY

45 -   **Page number**

45a - **Left side of page**

45b - **Right side of page**

45 -   **Groups only**

101a

A1

Alnwick
97b
98a

96a

Newcastle
upon Tyne

Durham

A1(M)

Middlesborough   Whitby

60b   60a   59b

61b

Richmond

A1

61a

Pickering   59a

Scarborough

Thirsk

63b

64a

York
58a,58b

Harrogate

Leeds   Hull
44a

Huddersfield

JERSEY
ACCOMMODATION CENTRE
16a

Close to the pretty fishing port of Gorey in St. Martins. With a range of B&B rooms from twin en suites to private dormitories and camping. The perfect mix for individuals or groups. Large communal WiFi lounge with TV & DVDs and a games room. Self catering kitchen, sauna, laundry. Packed lunches and adventure activities can be pre-ordered.

DETAILS
- **Open** - March-Oct. Reception 9am-4pm or 8pm depending on the season.
- **Beds** - 110: Bunks: 1x10, 6x8, 1x6, 4x4. Ensuite: 1x8, 1x5, 1x4, 2x3, 4x2, 2x1
- **Price/night** - B&B: £37pp (dorm), £39 (single en suite) £39 (twin/double en-suite, £10 single supplement). Youth groups of 20+ staying 2+ nights £33.

CONTACT: Ina
Tel: 01534 498636
info@jerseyhostel.co.uk
www.jerseyhostel.co.uk
La Rue de la Pouclee et des Quatre Chemins, St Martins, Jersey, JE3 6DU

LANDS END
HOSTEL
16b

Land's End Hostel, in the hamlet of Trevescan, is 1/2 mile from Land's End.

Double glazed & centrally heated, it has a fully equipped kitchen & dining areas inside & out.

Modern bathrooms and bedrooms with TVs & WiFi. New bunk beds with USB ports & LED lights. Bedding / towels supplied. Bike storage with CCTV, parking & small onsite shop.

DETAILS
- **Open** - All year.
- **Beds** - 14: 2×2,1×4,1×6 ensuite, 1 B&B
- **Price/night** - From £39pp, continental breakfast £7.50. Private rooms from £69.

CONTACT: Niko
Tel: 07585 625774
hello@landsendholidays.co.uk
www.landsendholidays.co.uk
Mill Barn, Trevescan, Sennen, Nr Land's End, Penzance, TR19 7AQ

LOWER PENDERLEATH
FARM HOSTEL
17a

Just three miles from St Ives' beaches & 5 miles from Penzance, Lower Penderleath Farm Hostel provides self-catering accommodation in four twin rooms and one alpine dormitory for 12. Plus a self contained family maisonette with small kitchen and private shower & toilet. BYO sleeping bags.

Pub food in two local villages is within walking distance. Bedding not provided.

DETAILS
- **Open** - May-Sept. Arrive between 9am-6pm, depart by 10am.
- **Beds** - 24: 4x2 + dorm platform of 12, 1x4 self contained maisonette
- **Price/night** - £23 dormitory. £48 private room sleeping 2. £130 Maisonette sleeping 4. Minimum of 2 nights stay.

CONTACT: Russell Rogers
rusrogers60@gmail.com
stivescampingandhostel.com
Lower Penderleath Farm, Towednack, St.Ives, Cornwall, TR26 3AF

COHORT
ST IVES
17b

Located in the centre of St Ives, Cohort is stylish and comfortable. Great facilities include a hot shower in the courtyard for surfers, through to a laundry & dry room. The on-site bar is cheap. There's a big guest kitchen, free super fast WiFi, a TV room & comfortable pod beds - all with USB ports, lights, curtains & under-bed storage. Free tea & coffee before 10am. Walk outside to find cafés, bars, galleries, Tate St Ives and four spectacular beaches. The SW Coast Path is 5 minutes from the front door.

DETAILS
- **Open** - Open all year
- **Beds** - 60: 1x8, 7x6, 1x4, 2x twin, 1x twin/double/triple
- **Price/night** - From £23

CONTACT: Reception
Tel: 01736 791664 or 07855 490831
hello@stayatcohort.co.uk
www.stayatcohort.co.uk
The Stennack, St Ives, Cornwall, TR26 1FF

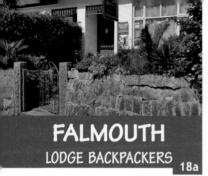

FALMOUTH
LODGE BACKPACKERS
18a

Relaxed, friendly and clean, Falmouth Lodge is just two minutes' walk from the Blue Flag Gyllyngvase beach and the South West Coast Path. Only eight minutes' walk into town with its exotic gardens, art galleries, Maritime Museum, Pendennis Castle and the harbour. Free parking and WiFi. Complimentary tea and coffee. Well-equipped kitchen, lovely dining room and cosy lounge.

DETAILS
■ **Open** - All year for sole use. Otherwise, closed from 15 Nov - 15 Feb. Weekly bookings changeovers on Fridays.
■ **Beds** - 14: 1x dbl; 1xdbl en suite, 1x2/3; 1x3/4 1x4/5;.
■ **Price/night** - Sole use from £350 per night, with discounts for 7 nights or more.

CONTACT: Judi
Tel: 07525 722808
judi@falmouthlodge.co.uk
www.falmouthbackpackers.co.uk
9 Gyllyngvase Terrace, Falmouth, Cornwall, TR11 4DL

EDENS YARD
BACKPACKERS
18b

Edensyard takes inspiration from the Camino; even the most self-sufficient traveller needs a recharge and TLC.

Need a basecamp for your Cornish adventure? No problem: we are a short leafy lane from the Eden Project and busses that will take you to St Austell's onward travel hub.

Head out with friends, chill out with family. Come find our hostel in the strange landscape and clay trials of mid Cornwall.

DETAILS
■ **Open** - Open from Spring 2023
■ **Beds** - 14: in two rooms
■ **Price/night** - £20 per person.

CONTACT: Neal or Julia
Tel: 01726 814907   or 07958 037357
info@edensyard.uk
www.edensyard.uk
17 Tregrehan Mills, St. Austell, Cornwall, PL25 3TL

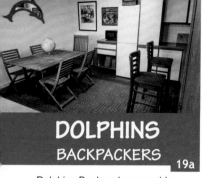

DOLPHINS
BACKPACKERS
19a

Dolphins Backpackers provides affordable accommodation just ten minutes from the South West Coast Path in the centre of scenic coastal village of Tintagel. It is just five minutes' walk from the castle, famous for King Arthur's legends, myth and folklore.

The hostel sleeps up to 13 in mixture of private and dorm rooms. There is a welcoming atmosphere in the shared kitchen, the communal areas and the large covered garden. Basic breakfast provided, cooked breakfasts available.

DETAILS
- **Open** - All year
- **Beds** - 13: 1x1, 1x2, 1x10
- **Price/night** - From £34

CONTACT: John
Tel: 07740 976326
hello@dolphinsbackpackers.co.uk
www.dolphinsbackpackers.co.uk
Dolphins Backpackers, Fore Street,
Tintagel, Cornwall, PL34 0DB

BACHELORS
HALL
19b

Set in a beautiful secluded valley in Dartmoor National Park, Bachelors Hall offers groups of all kind the chance to experience the freedom of the moor and the vastness of the landscape.

Formerly run as a tradition youth hostel, it was completely refurbished in 2019. Sleeping 60 across 6 rooms and 2 pods it is centrally heated with a commercial kitchen and large separate dining room/classroom. Outdoor activities can be organised if required.

     GROUPS ONLY

DETAILS
- **Open** - All year.
- **Beds** - 60: 1x14, 1x10, 2x6, 3x4. Pods: 2x6
- **Price/night** - £420 for up to 35 guests and then £12pp up to 60 max

CONTACT: Rosie Broughton
Tel: 01237 429501
RBroughton@athenalearningtrust.uk
www.bachelorshall.co.uk
Princetown, Yelverton, Devon. PL20 6SL

SPARROWHAWK
BACKPACKERS
20a

A small, friendly eco-hostel in the centre of Moretonhampstead, Dartmoor National Park. Popular with cyclists, hikers, bikers, wild swimmers, artists and photographers, A beautifully converted stone stable, with solar-heated showers, kitchen, courtyard, BBQ and secure bike shed. High open moorland, rocky tors, ancient burial sites, stone circles, woods and clear rivers close by.

Moretonhampstead has shops, cafés, art galleries and pubs. On the Cicerone LEJOG, Dartmoor Way and CTC routes.

DETAILS
- **Open** - All year
- **Beds** - 12: 1x12
- **Price/night** - Adult dorm £25

CONTACT: Alison
Tel: 01647 440318 or 07870 513570
sparrowhawkbarn@gmail.com
www.sparrowhawkbackpackers.co.uk
45 Ford Street, Moretonhampstead,
Dartmoor, Devon, TQ13 8LN

EXETER GLOBE
BACKPACKERS
20b

Globe Backpackers offers clean, comfortable, self catering accommodation for up to 30. Book a bed, a room or the whole place.

It is just a few minutes' walk from Exeter's city centre with its cathedral, picturesque historic waterway, quay and wide range of shops, pubs, clubs, cafés and restaurants.

DETAILS
- **Open** - All year (phone for Xmas). Check in 3.30 - 7.30pm (earlier or later by arrangement only).
- **Beds** - 30: 3 private rooms and 5 dormitories.
- **Price/night** - £22.50 per night (dorm). From £100 per week (dorm). From £55 per night (private room)

CONTACT: Duty Manager
Tel: 01392 215521
info@exeterbackpackers.co.uk
www.exeterbackpackers.co.uk
71 Holloway Street, Exeter, EX2 4JD

ASHCLYST FARM
HOSTEL
21a

Ashclyst Farm Hostel is a charming National Trust farm house on an organic arable farm at the edge of Ashclyst Forest.

The hostel sleeps between 9 and 11 people in double, twin and single rooms. The beds are fully made up with duvets and the bedrooms are spacious and quiet.

Guests have full use of the farmhouse kitchen, dining rooms and lounge.

DETAILS
- **Open** - Spring, Summer, Autumn.
- **Beds** - 9: 2 x doubles, 7 x single
- **Price/night** - From £27pp. Twin/double rooms from £54. Entire house from £300

CONTACT: Lorraine or Martyn.
Tel: 01392 461302
lorraineglover@hotmail.co.uk
www.ashclystfarmhostel.com
Harepathstead Rd, Broadclyst, East Devon, EX5 3DF

ELMSCOTT
HOSTEL
21b

Elmscott Hostel is surrounded by unspoiled coastline with sea views of Lundy Island. Great for walking, cycling, surfing and bird watching. The South West Coast Path is just a few mins' walk away. The hostel is well equipped for all your self-catering needs and has a games room and shop. In winter it is only available for sole use bookings.

DETAILS
- **Open** - All year.
- **Beds** - 32 (35 in winter): 1 unit of 20: 2x6, 2x4; 1 unit of 12: 1x6, 1x4, 1x2. Extra 3 bed room for sole use in winter.
- **Price/night** - Adult £27-£30, under 16s £20-£23. Discounts for groups or longer stays.

CONTACT: John, Thirza and Kate
Tel: 01237 441367 or 01237 441276 or Kate 01237 441637
john.goa@virgin.net
www.elmscott.org.uk
Elmscott, Hartland, Bideford, Devon, EX39 6ES

YARDE ORCHARD
BUNKHOUSE & CAMPING 22a

Yarde Orchard provides accommodation and refreshments to those using the Tarka Trail with good access to the great North Devon beaches and Dartmoor. The bunkhouse has an en suite double room with its own entrance, a bunk room sleeping four, a twin room for two, and a campsite. You can enjoy home-cooked meals and the relaxed café atmosphere on the terrace.

DETAILS
■ **Open** - Bunkhouse open all year. Camping April - September.
■ **Beds** - 6:1xdbl, 1x4, 1x2 plus camping.
■ **Price/night** - 4 berth bunkroom £80, single occupancy £40, double occupancy £60. Double room £80. Camping £15pp. Dogs please enquire for price.

CONTACT: Michelle Stewart
Tel: 01805 621111
yardeorchard1@gmail.com
www.yarde-orchard.co.uk
East Yarde, Peters Marland, Torrington, Devon, EX38 8QA

SEALOCK BARN
22b

This converted workshop on a restored section of the heritage Rolle canal in rural Devon sleeps up to 10 in 3 rooms. Surrounded by a county wildlife site & salt marshes there is abundant wildlife.

Facilities include an open plan kitchen/living/dining area and two WC/shower rooms. The barn has direct access to the Tarka Trail, perfect for walking or cycling. Guests will also enjoy direct access to the tidal River Torridge for canoeing & fishing. BYO sleeping bags.

DETAILS

■ **Open** - All year.
■ **Beds** - 10: 1x4, 2x3 + camping
■ **Price/night** - £10pp midweek, £12 pp weekend. Enquire for whole barn

CONTACT: Hilary Wills
Tel: 01237 477705
hilarywills@yahoo.co.uk
Vale Cottage, 7 Annery Kiln, Weare Giffard, Bideford, EX39 5JE.

OCEAN
BACKPACKERS
23a

23b
ROCK AND RAPID
BUNKHOUSE

Very close to the picturesque Ilfracombe Harbour, this cosy, cool, clean and friendly hostel offers fantastic facilities for groups, families, and sole travellers. There is storage and a drying room for wetsuits bikes & boards. Plenty of books, games & USB ports. A well equipped self-catering kitchen and a spacious living room with free WiFi. A real home form home. Close to restaurants & bars.

DETAILS

- **Open** - All year (exclusive hire only Nov-Mar inclusive). Check in 4pm to 7pm.
- **Beds** - 45: mix of dorms / family rooms
- **Price/night** - Dorms from £26pp. Double/twin rooms from £66 a room for bookings made via our website. Contact by email/phone for group bookings.

CONTACT: Alex and Gavin
Tel: 07775 501878
alexmcwb@icloud.com
www.oceanbackpackers.co.uk
29 St James Place, Ilfracombe, Devon, EX34 9BJ

Perfect for an adventurous or relaxing break. The Rock and Rapid Adventure Centre offers activities such as climbing (climbing wall on site for lessons or use by experienced climbers) coasteering, raft building and canoeing. The bunkhouse can be rented out for sole use, or an activity package can be put together for your group. This can vary from a few activities to a full programme, including food. Just 20 mins from the North Devon coastline. Hen and stags welcome as are family and school groups.

    GROUPS ONLY

DETAILS

- **Open** - All year. 24 hours.
- **Beds** - 40: 2x18, 2x2
- **Price/night** - Sole use £285 for single nights and £260 for multiple nights

CONTACT: Keith Crockford
Tel: 01769 309003
info@rockandrapidadventures.co.uk
www.rockandrapidadventures.co.uk
Hacche Mill, South Molton, EX36 3NA

NORTHCOMBE
CAMPING BARNS
24a

EXMOOR
BUNKBARN
24b

A mile outside the town of Dulverton on Exmoor, Northcombe Camping Barns nestle in the Barle river valley with good canoeing, walking and bridleways.

A perfect base for groups on Exmoor. The barns sleep 16 and 28 in partitioned dormitories. Smaller groups can be catered for. Heated by wood-burning stoves with a well equipped kitchen, you just need to bring your own pillows, sleeping bags or duvets.

Formerly a granary on a working farm, this eco-friendly bunkbarn is close to Winsford Hill and Wimbleball lake. Perfect for exploring Exmoor on foot, bike or canoe. Hot water, central heating & WiFi included in price. Well equipped, open-plan kitchen/dinning with seating for all. Large drying room. Outside BBQ area and small field with campfire. BYO bedding & towels. Sleeps max 25 - sole use only. Free logs for the stove and camp fire. Enjoy Exmoor's dark skies.

DETAILS

DETAILS

■ **Open** - All year. Arrive after 4pm, depart before 10.30am
■ **Beds** - 44: Barn16: 1x6, 1x10. Barn28: 1x6, 1x10, 1x12
■ **Price/night** - Sole use: Barn16 from £170. Barn28 from £270. Showers 20p. Electric meter £1 coins.

CONTACT: Sally Harvey
Tel: 01398 323602
sallyeharvey17@gmail.com
Hollam, Dulverton, Somerset, TA22 9JH

■ **Open** - All year. All day.
■ **Beds** - 25: 1x14, 1x8, 1x3
■ **Price/night** - Whole barn only:- Weekend (2 nights minimum) £400 per night. Weekdays £350 per night.

CONTACT: Julia or Guy Everard
Tel: 01643 851410 or 07967 114331
bookings@exmoorbunkbarn.co.uk
www.exmoorbunkbarn.co.uk
Week Farm, Bridgetown, Dulverton
TA22 9JP

BASE LODGE

25a

Base Lodge is your perfect base for exploring Exmoor, the Quantocks and North Devon. The South West Coast Path starts in Minehead and there is excellent mountain biking.

Guided biking, navigational training, climbing, surfing, pony trekking and natural history walks can all be arranged. Base Lodge is clean, comfortable with self-catering and a cosy log burner.

DETAILS

- **Open** - All year. All day access once booked (reception open from 3pm).
- **Beds** - 22: 1x7, 1x6, 1x5, 2x2
- **Price/night** - Dorms £20 (£25 one night), private single £7.50 supplement, twin/double £40. Sole use of Base Lodge from £200. Family room discount.

CONTACT: Wendy or Graham
Tel: 01643 703520 or 07731 651536
togooutdoors@hotmail.com
16 The Parks, Minehead, Somerset,
TA24 8BS

MONKTON WYLD
COURT

25b

This Victorian neo-Gothic mansion in Dorset's AONB has easy access to the Jurassic Coast at Lyme Regis as well as the Wessex and Monarch's Way long distance footpaths. Guests can use the vegetarian self-catering kitchen to prepare their own meals or vegetarian meals can be pre-booked. There is also camping in the grounds. Run by a charity that promotes sustainable living. Fruit and vegetables are grown in the organic garden and Jersey cows provide the dairy products.

DETAILS

- **Open** - All year. Office opening hours: 9am-5pm.
- **Beds** - 42 beds in various room sizes.
- **Price/night** - £40pp

CONTACT: Office Team
Tel: 01297 560342
info@monktonwyldcourt.org
www.monktonwyldcourt.co.uk
Elsdon's Lane, Monkton Wyld, Nr
Charmouth, Dorset, DT6 6DQ

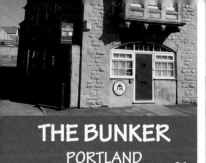

THE BUNKER
PORTLAND
26a

26b

MYTIME
OUTDOOR CENTRE

The Bunker is on the South West Coastal Path, with Chesil Beach on its doorstep and world class sport climbing, diving sites and water-sports a short distance away. Sleeping up to 18 in 6 private bunk rooms, each with a shower and sink, The Bunker offers affordable accommodation for groups and individuals. It has a large communal area, kitchen with tea and coffee and free WiFi. Breakfast and packed lunches available when booked in advance.

Surrounded by open farmland & a short walk from the Jurassic Coast, MYTIME's R&R Retreat Accommodation Centre offers the perfect base for enjoying the spectacular Isle of Purbeck. With a World Heritage Site & the South West Coastal Path on its doorstep, it is perfect for outdoor enthusiasts. Just minutes from the idyllic village of Worth Matravers and the popular Square and Compass Pub, there's truly something for everyone.

DETAILS
- **Open** - All year. Check in from 15:00, check out by 10:00
- **Beds** - 18: 3x4,3x2, private bunkrooms
- **Price/night** - Ranging from £35 - £70 per room. Exclusive hire available.

DETAILS
- **Open** - All year.
- **Beds** - 24: 1x2, 1x4 en suite, 1x8, 1x10. Plus 16 camping.
- **Price/night** - Whole centre from £350 (24 people). Plus camping (BYO tents) at £7pppn. Bedding £5pp. Dog £10.

CONTACT: Tony or Sally
Tel: 07846 401010
stay@thebunkerportland.com
www.thebunkerportland.com
The Bunker, Victoria Square, Portland, Dorset, DT5 1AL

CONTACT: MYTIME
Tel: 01202 710701
enquiries@mytimeyoungcarers.org
www.mytimeyoungcarers.org
Off Renscombe Rd, Worth Matravers, Isle of Purbeck, Dorset. BH19 3LL

SWANAGE
AUBERGE
27a

27b
CUMULUS
CENTRE

Family run, Swanage Auberge is a refuge for climbers, cyclists, walkers & divers at the eastern end of the Jurassic Coast. In the centre of Swanage, a stone's throw from the South West Coast Path, there is excellent walking, mountain biking, diving and rock climbing close by. There is a fully equipped self-catering kitchen and a packed lunch service if required. Parking for 2 vehicles is available on a first come first served basis & free on-street parking is close by.

Cumulus Outdoor Residential Centre is situated in the small seaside town of Swanage on Dorset's Jurassic Coast. The purpose built centre sits in 6 acres of private grounds and has 4 separate accommodation units sleeping 16,32,32 or 47 which can be hired individually or together. The centre is popular with groups of friends/families, schools, youth groups, DofE & corporate groups. A whole range of outdoor activities are available for your group if required. Dogs welcome with prior arrangement.

DETAILS

- **Open** - All year (phone mobile if no reply). All day.
- **Beds** - 15: 1x6, 1x4,1x5
- **Price/night** - £30 first night then £25. Inc bedding/towel, cereal breakfast, tea & coffee. Group rates. No credit cards.

CONTACT: Pam
Tel: 01929 424368 or 07803 739819
bookings@swanageauberge.co.uk
www.swanageauberge.co.uk
45 High St, Swanage, Dorset, BH19 2LX

DETAILS

- **Open** - All year.
- **Beds** - 133: Bungalow 16: plus others.
- **Price/night** - Bungalow - £256, enquire for other buildings.

CONTACT: Julia Munn
Tel: 01929 422480
sam@cumulusoutdoors.com
www.cumulusoutdoors.com
Cobbler's Lane, Swanage, Dorset
BH19 2PX

STONEHENGE
HOSTEL
28a

28b
MENDIP
BUNKHOUSE

Welcome to Stonehenge Hostel, family farm & vineyards, where the perfect overnight accommodation awaits! Set in over 40 acres of stunning Wiltshire countryside, vineyards, farm & woodlands, the hostel is located just 8 miles from the historic city of Salisbury and is only 5 miles from the iconic Stonehenge.

Come along and enjoy the rare breed farm animals, vineyards and over 70 beds in the fantastic Stonehenge Hostel.

DETAILS
- **Open** - All year
- **Beds** - 70: 2x2, 1x3, 5x4, 1x5, 1x6 + dorms
- **Price/night** - Enquire for prices.

CONTACT: Reception
Tel: 01980 629438
marketing@choldertonrarebreedsfarm.com
www.stonehengehostel.co.uk
Beacon House, Amesbury Road,
Cholderton, Salisbury, Wilts, SP4 0EW

Larkshall (Mendip Bunkhouse) is the Cerberus Spelaeological Society's HQ. It offers well appointed comfortable accommodation on The Mendips, perfect for caving, walking, cycling, climbing, diving at Vobster Quay and for exploring the Somerset countryside. Local attractions include Wells, Wookey Hole, Cheddar Gorge, Glastonbury & Bath. Camping available. Ample parking.

DETAILS
- **Open** - All year. All day.
- **Beds** - 30+: 1x5, 1x6, 1x8, 1x14 (plus camping).
- **Price/night** - £10 + 50% for single nights. Min 2 nights at weekends. Enquire for sole use of a bunkroom. Discounts for BMC or BCA members.

CONTACT:
Tel: 08454 750954
hostelbookings@cerberusspeleo.org.uk
www.cerberusspeleo.org.uk
Cerberus Spelaeological Soc., Larkshall,
Fosse Rd. Oakhill, Somerset, BA3 5HY

BATH YMCA

29a

THE BRISTOL
WING

29b

Bath YMCA offers great value accommodation. Centrally located, all the sights of this World Heritage city are easily reached on foot. With 210 beds, Bath YMCA specialises in making guests feel comfortable. Fully air conditioned lounge with TV, laundry, lockers, football table and WiFi.

Couples, families, groups and backpackers all welcome.

DETAILS

- **Open** - All year. All day.
- **Beds** - 210: Dorms: 1x10, 3x12, 1x15, 1x18. Rooms: 7 x quad, 6 x triple, 29 x twin, 5 x double, 9 x single
- **Price/night** - Dorm from £20pp (£25 at weekends), Private rooms from £34 (£38 at weekends). Includes breakfast.

CONTACT: Reception
Tel: 01225 325900
stay@ymcabathgroup.org.uk
www.ymcabath.org.uk
International House, Broad Street Place, Bath, BA1 5LH

The Bristol Wing is reopening in 2023, providing accommodation for independent travellers, groups and tourists.

This iconic police headquarters provides chic accommodation in the heart of Bristol. A mix of private, en suite and dorm rooms with communal spaces and a cafe.

Close to the bus station, and perfectly located for Bristol's best attractions and shopping from big names to quirky markets.

DETAILS

- **Open** - Bristol Wing is reopening in April 2023.
- **Beds** - 88
- **Price/night** - Enquire for pirce

CONTACT: Reception
Tel: 0117 428 6199
www.thebristolwing.co.uk
9 Bridewell Street, Bristol, BS1 2QD

COURT HILL
CENTRE
30a

Only a few steps from the historic Ridgeway National Trail, Court Hill Centre enjoys breathtaking views over the Vale of the White Horse. Reclaimed barns surround a pretty courtyard garden.

Providing accommodation for schools, families, groups and individuals, the centre offers evening meals, breakfasts and picnic lunches. There is a beautiful high-roofed dining room which retains the atmosphere of the old barn. A meeting/class-room, camping and self-catering kitchen are also available.

DETAILS

■ **Open** - All year. To check availability please call 01235 760253.
■ **Beds** - 59: 1x15,1x9,1x6,1x5,6x4,1x2
■ **Price/night** - From £22.50. U18 £15.50

CONTACT: Reception
Tel: 01235 760253
info@courthill.org.uk
www.courthill.org.uk
Letcombe Regis, Wantage, OX12 9NE

WETHERDOWN
LODGE & CAMPSITE
30b

An award winning eco-renovation in the heart of the South Downs National Park right on the South Downs Way. The perfect base for walkers, cyclists, business away-days and family get-togethers. The lodge offers well appointed self-catering accommodation. There are also newly refurbished B&B rooms and a campsite with yurts and secluded woodland pitches. Large grounds with woodland trails and a café. Pubs, shops & take-aways within 2 miles

DETAILS

■ **Open** - Lodge, B&B and Campsite are open all year. Yurts from Apr to Oct.
■ **Beds** - 62: Lodge 38: 14 rooms. B&B 24:12 rooms. Camping & Yurts sleep 36 .
■ **Price/night** - See website.

CONTACT: Reception
Tel: 01730 823549 or 01730 823166
accommodation@sustainability-centre.org
www.sustainability-centre.org
The Sustainability Centre, East Meon, Hampshire, GU32 1HR

GAVESTON
HALL
31a

PUTTENHAM BARN
BUNKHOUSE
31b

A former boarding school nestling in beautiful countryside, Gaveston Hall accommodates groups of all sizes. The 100 beds are spread across dorms, private single/twin rooms & chalets. Set in magnificent grounds with a football field, tennis court, woodland walks and fishing lake. Inside there are table tennis & pool tables and an indoor swimming pool (summer only). Room for coach parking.

Puttenham Barn Bunkhouse on the North Downs Way offers simple accommodation for walkers & cyclists in the Surrey Hills AONB. A converted historic barn with a volunteer warden to welcome you. Pub food in the village. Garden, picnic bench & secure cycle shed. No cars allowed on site but there is limited street parking nearby. Railway stations: Wanborough (3.5 km) & Guildford (7km).

 GROUPS ONLY

DETAILS
- **Open** - Closed January.
- **Beds** - 100: Hall: 1x18,1x16 1x14 2xdbl, 1xtwin, 1xsgl. Chalets: 2x10, 1x13, 1x14
- **Price/night** - From £25pp. Small extra charge for bedding hire or BYO.

DETAILS
- **Open** - Arrive after 5pm leave by 10am. No access 10am-5pm.
- **Beds** - 11 : 4x2 (bunk beds), 1x3/4 (sleeping platform) .
- **Price/night** - £20pp. Under 18 £15pp. £3 green discount pppn

CONTACT: Rita Barclay
Tel: 01403 891 431   or 07957 440 781
gavestonhall@outlook.com
www.gavestonhallsussex.com
Nuthurst, Horsham, West Sussex
RH13 6RF

CONTACT: Bookings
Tel: 01483 811001
book@puttenhambarn.uk
puttenhambarn.uk
The Street, Puttenham, Nr Guildford,
Surrey, GU3 1AR

PALACE FARM
HOSTEL
32a

Palace Farm Hostel is a relaxing, flexible 4* hostel on a family run farm.

Situated in the village of Doddington, (which has a pub!), in the North Kent Downs AONB. The area is great for walking, cycling & wildlife. There are ten fully heated en suite rooms sleeping up to 39. Duvets, linen and continental breakfast included.

DETAILS
- **Open** - All year. 8am to 10pm. Flexible, please ask.
- **Beds** - 39: 1x8, 1x6, 2x5 (family room), 1x4, 1x3 and 4x2
- **Price/night** - From £16-£40pp (all private en suite rooms). Group reductions.

CONTACT: Graham and Liz Cuthbert
Tel: 01795 886200
info@palacefarm.com
www.palacefarm.com
Down Court Road, Doddington,
Sittingbourne, Faversham, Kent,
ME9 0AU

PUBLOVE
@ THE WHITE FERRY
32b

The White Ferry House is a stunning Victorian flat-iron building steeped in history. It provides accommodation in central London, close to Victoria, The Houses of Parliament and Buckingham Palace. In the traditional pub atmosphere you can enjoy chilling out and playing board games, locally sourced drinks and award-winning burgers. There's a 24 hour reception, free WiFi, individual power sockets and guest food & drink discounts. Publove@The White Ferry offers a classic night out and a great location for exploring London by day.

DETAILS
- **Open** - All year.
- **Beds** - 75: 1x3, 1x6, 2x9, 4x12
- **Price/night** - From £15 per person.

CONTACT: The Bar
Tel: 020 7233 6133
whiteferry@publove.co.uk
www.publove.co.uk
The White Ferry House, 1 Sutherland Street, London, SW1V 4LD

HARLOW
INTERNATIONAL
33a

33b

1912 CENTRE

Harlow International Hostel is in the centre of a landscaped park and is one of the oldest buildings in Harlow. The town of Harlow is your ideal base for exploring London, Cambridge and the best of South East England. The journey time to central London is only 35 minutes from the hostel door and it is the closest hostel to Stansted Airport. National Cycle Route 1 passes the front door. Meals can be provided for groups. There's a children's zoo, orienteering course and outdoor pursuits centre in the park.

The 1912 Centre is the former Harwich fire station with views to the harbour.

The centrally heated hostel offers a large dining / recreational area and cabin style rooms, with two ground floor rooms suitable for disabled. Facilities include a fully equipped kitchen, showers & drying room. BYO sleeping bag. The Centre is close to town amenities, Harwich Town railway station and 50m from the promenade and sandy beach.

DETAILS

- **Open** - All year. 8am - 10.30pm (check in 3-10.30pm).
- **Beds** - 30: 2x1, 5x2, 1x4, 1x6, 1x8
- **Price/night** - Please see the website.

DETAILS

- **Open** - All year.
- **Beds** - 26: 3x6, 2x2, 1x4.
- **Price/night** - 1 night £290, 2 nights £540, 5 nights £1075, 7 nights £1350. Other prices on application.

CONTACT: Richard Adams
Tel: 01279 421702
mail@h-i-h.co.uk
www.h-i-h.co.uk
13 School Lane, Harlow, Essex
CM20 2QD

CONTACT: Debbie Hill
Tel: 01255 552010
info@harwichconnexions.co.uk
www.harwichconnexions.co.uk
Cow Lane, Off Kings Quay Street,
Harwich CO12 3ES

DARSHAM
COUNTRY CENTRE
34a

OLD BROODER
BUNKHOUSE
34b

Darsham Country Centre is in the old railway station. Affiliated with the Woodcraft Folk, the Centre provides affordable self catering accommodation for groups of up to 24. It is perfectly situated for exploring the beauty of the Suffolk countryside & visiting the area's many tourist attractions. Suffolk's Heritage Coast & the market town of Saxmundham are only 5-6 miles away. Overflow camping for up to 15.

Comfy, farm stay self-catering in rural, but train-accessible, Suffolk. Sleeps 22 in five bedrooms, including a restored Shepherd's Hut. Mix of oak bunks & beds. Relax in cosy sitting room; croquet, BBQ, ping-pong & badminton; explore the farm, picnic in a meadow. 20 bikes included in hire or kayak down the River Stour. Go Ape, visit castles, coast, historic towns. Larger groups can also book the Tudor Barn (also in this guide).

DETAILS

- **Open** - All year.
- **Beds** - 24: 2x5, 3x4, 2x1
- **Price/night** - Charities/voluntary groups: £170. Statutory groups: £250. Private groups: W/end & BH: £385. Sun-Thurs: £275

DETAILS

- **Open** - Check booking arrangements
- **Beds** - 22: 3x2, 2x8
- **Price/night** - W/ends: 2 nights min from £1250. 3 nights Bank Hols £2,700. 2 nights m/week from £900. Ask for a quote for small groups or 1-night stays.

CONTACT: Annette Day
Tel: 07941 640796 or 01728 668736
darsham@woodcraft.org.uk
www.darshamcountrycentre.org.uk
Main Road Darsham Saxmundham,
Suffolk. IP17 3JU

CONTACT: Juliet Hawkins
Tel: 01787 247235
hawkins@thehall-milden.co.uk
www.thehall-milden.co.uk
The Hall, Milden, Lavenham, Sudbury,
Suffolk CO10 9NY

TUDOR BARN

35a

The Tudor Barn offers atmospheric group accommodation on an environmentally friendly working farm in rural Suffolk. Sleeping 23+ (singles/doubles/4 posters) in 4 private rooms plus the huge space of the Tudor Barn where you also feast and relax. The perfect base for group celebrations, reunions or activity breaks. Bikes and Tudor costumes are included. Larger parties can sleep 22 additional guests at the Old Brooder Bunkhouse 100m down the track (also in this guide).

DETAILS

- **Open** - Check booking arrangements
- **Beds** - 23+: 3x2, 1x1, 1x16. (+cots)
- **Price/night** - W/ends: 2 nights £1,500 to £2,285. 2 nights midweek from £1,150. Enquire for small groups & 1 night stays.

CONTACT: Juliet Hawkins
Tel: 01787 247235
hawkins@thehall-milden.co.uk
www.thehall-milden.co.uk
The Hall, Milden, Lavenham, Sudbury,
Suffolk CO10 9NY

OUTDOOR INNS
LIDGATE

35b

Stay in a cosy eco-cabin next to a characterful 16th-century village pub in the Suffolk countryside.

The two cabins in the grounds of The Star at Lidgate both sleep 6 in two twin rooms and 2 single sofa beds.

There are 2 shower rooms and a fully equipped kitchenette with a hob and fridge, a private terrace, outdoor seating and a secure bike shed. All linens and towels are provided. Dogs welcome.

DETAILS

- **Open** - All year
- **Beds** - 12: 2 x 6 person cabins
- **Price/night** - £120 per cabin (sleeps 6). Min stay 2 nights

CONTACT: Josh
Tel: 020 7363 1144
info@outdoorinns.com
outdoorinns.com/sites/star-at-lidgate
The Star, The Street, Lidgate,
Newmarket, Suffolk, CB8 9PP.

OLD RED LION

36a

The medieval walled town of Castle Acre is on the Peddars Way ancient track/long distance path. This former pub, continues to serve travellers who seek refreshment and repose. Stay in private rooms and enjoy a quiet communal snug or 2 large areas suitable for group activities.

DETAILS

■ **Open** - All year. All day. Arrival times by arrangement.
■ **Beds** - 14: 1x6, 3 x twin, 1x double, 2x double ensuite
■ **Price/night** - Double ensuite £80. Double room £70. Twin room £60. Family room with 6 single beds, £35 per bed. All prices include self-service breakfast and packed lunch. Enquire for sole use.

CONTACT: Alison Loughlin
Tel: 01760 755557
oldredlion@yahoo.co.uk
www.oldredlion.org.uk
Old Red Lion, Bailey Street, Castle Acre, Norfolk, PE32 2AG

DEEPDALE
ROOMS & CAMPING

36b

Deepdale Rooms offers a range of comfortable, private, self catering rooms. Choose from double, twin, triple, quad, family & larger rooms for small groups. Most rooms are en suite. All bedding is provided, BYO towels. Facilities include a large well equipped kitchen, communal dining area & living room, underfloor heating throughout & laundry/drying facilities. There's also an adjoining campsite. Large groups by arrangement.

DETAILS

■ **Open** - All year. All day. Collect key from Deepdale Visitor Information Centre
■ **Beds** - 60: 13 x dbl, 3 twin, 4 triple, 5 quad, 4 family quad, 2 small group
■ **Price/night** - From £42 per private room

CONTACT: Deepdale Rooms & Camping
Tel: 01485 210256
stay@deepdalecamping.co.uk
www.deepdalebackpackers.co.uk
Deepdale Farm, Burnham Deepdale, Norfolk, PE31 8DD

CHELLINGTON
CENTRE
37a

CROFT FARM
WATERPARK
37b

A unique venue for sole-use groups to stay in an ancient, Grade I listed church. The Centre sleeps 36 in bunkrooms (plus 30 camping, further charges apply). Modern facilities, self-catering kitchen & breakout lounges. Situated in the beautiful Bedfordshire countryside with amazing views. Easily accessible from the M1 but a world apart. Good disabled access. Youth group discounts.

Just outside Tewkesbury in the scenic River Avon Valley, with it's own lake. Accommodation is in cabins, a pod village, chalets & camping. Great for touring the Cotswolds, Malverns, Bredon Hill & the Forest of Dean. A wide range of watersports, activities & tuition are on offer. A footpath meanders through the meadow to the River Avon and free river fishing is available to guests.

DETAILS

- **Open** - All year. Arrive 5pm. Leave by 2pm.
- **Beds** - 36: 2x5, 5x4, 1x6 + 30 camping
- **Price/night** - Youth groups: week night £495-650, weekend £550-650 (Fri & Sat min). Other Groups: week night £630-750, weekend (2 night min) £750-900.

DETAILS

- **Open** - All year. 9am-9pm.
- **Beds** - 216: Chalets: (4 pers) x32, twin x8. Cabins (8 pers) x5. Pod (4 pers) x8
- **Price/night** - Pod/Chalet (4 pers) £50 (£65 for 1 night). Chalet (twin) £50 (£65/1 night). Cabin (8 pers en suite) £120 (£140/1 night)

CONTACT: Scott or Debbie
Tel: 01234 720726
admin@chellington.org
www.chellington.org
St Nicholas Church, Felmersham Road, Carlton, Bedford MK43 7NA

CONTACT: Martin Newell
Tel: 01684 772321 or 07736 036967
info@croftfarmwaterpark.com
www.croftfarmwaterpark.com
Bredons Hardwick, Near Tewkesbury, Gloucestershire GL20 7EE

STATION COTTAGE
COLWALL
38a

Station Cottage is a small eco hostel in the Malvern Hills ANOB. Individuals, couples, families & small groups arriving by foot, bike or public transport are all welcomed (apologies, no cars).

Station Cottage is located next to Colwall Station with direct links to Birmingham, Oxford, Reading, London & Hereford. The cottage sleeps up to 8 in three rooms. All bedding and towels provided.

DETAILS
- **Open** - All year. Check in after 5pm. Check out before 10am.
- **Beds** - 8: 2 x twin, 1x1, 1x3 (campbeds)
- **Price/night** - £20 pp. Enquire for sole use or longer stays.

CONTACT: Rebecca Roseff
Tel: 07561 861578
stationcottagecolwall@gmail.com
www.stationcottagecolwall.co.uk
Station Cottage, Albert Road, Colwall, Herefordshire. WR13 6QS

DUNFIELD
HOUSE
38b

In rural Herefordshire, close to the Welsh border, Dunfield House provides accommodation for groups of up to 95 with sole use of the house, stables, parkland & swimming pool. From November to March the house & stables can also be hired individually.
The house provides fully catered accommodation & the stables have a self-catering kitchen. A great choice for school, youth, music or church groups, training courses & family get-togethers.

DETAILS
- **Open** - All year. All day. Closed for two weeks over Christmas.
- **Beds** - 95: Main house: 73. Stables: 22
- **Price/night** - Main House £1440 + £24pp full board. Stables £660. Whole site (sleeps 95) £2100 + £24pp full board.

CONTACT: The Reception Team
Tel: 01544 230563
info@dunfieldhouse.org.uk
www.dunfieldhouse.org.uk
Kington, Herefordshire. HR5 3NN

LUDLOW MASCALL
CENTRE
39a

A beautiful Victorian building in the heart of Ludlow, providing en suite accommodation within walking distance of restaurants, shops and pubs. Close to the Shropshire Hills and Mortimer Forest with their miles of stunning landscapes to explore. Fresh towels, bedlinen, complimentary toiletries, tea and coffee making facilities, parking and WiFi included. Residents also have access to a lounge, dining area, kitchen, and courtyard garden. Breakfasts available.

DETAILS
- **Open** - All year except NY and Xmas.
- **Beds** - 19: 1 family room (sleeps 4), 7 twin rooms, 1 single room
- **Price/night** - Family room (4 beds) from £72. Twin from £54. Single from £36.

CONTACT:
Tel: 01584 873882
info@ludlowmascallcentre.co.uk
www.ludlowmascallcentre.co.uk
Lower Galdeford, Ludlow, Shropshire
SY8 1RZ

HAYE FARM
SLEEPING BARN
39b

This bunkhouse on a working farm has a fully equipped self-catering kitchen, dining room and lounge. Enjoy the quiet rural location on the covered decking, patio (with BBQ) and lawn. The nearby Wye Forest is one of the largest remaining ancient forests in England. On the Worcestershire Way and close to the Severn Way and Mercian Way (NCN route 45) at Bewdley (1 mile). The West Midland Safari Park and Severn Valley Railway are also very close.

DETAILS
- **Open** - All year. 24 hour access.
- **Beds** - 15: 1x2, 1x3, 1x4, 1x6
- **Price/night** - From £25pp sole use. Smaller groups / private rooms may be available. Visit website for prices.

CONTACT: Stuart Norgrove
Tel: 7732489195
enquiries@haye-farm.co.uk
www.haye-farm.co.uk
Haye Farm, Ribbesford, Bewdley,
Worcestershire, DY12 2TP

BRIDGES
YOUTH HOSTEL
40a

40b

ALL STRETTON
BUNKHOUSE

In the Shropshire hills, close to Long Mynd & Stiperstones, Bridges Hostel is perfect for walkers. The Shropshire Way, the End to End cycle route & moutain bike routes pass close by.
The hostel has a self catering kitchen, lounge with wood fire, drying room, shop & large garden. Home cooked evening meals. Camping.

All Stretton Bunkhouse offers comfortable, cosy, self catering accommodation for groups of up to 10. It has easy access to the Long Mynd with walks & bike rides for all levels. The busy town of Church Stretton is a short drive & it's just 10 mins' walk to the local pub. There's a well equipped kitchen, a shower, two toilets & a tumble dryer. Dogs welcome with sole use.

DETAILS
■ **Open** - All year except Xmas. Reception:8-10am & 5-10pm. Hostel closes at 11pm.
■ **Beds** - 28: 2x4 en suite, 2x6, 1x8 plus camping
■ **Price/night** - New prices from 1.3.23: 4-bed ensuite: £110, £95 2+ nights. 6-bed: £135, £120 2+ nights. 8-bed: £170, £140 2+ nights.

CONTACT: Bridges Youth Hostel
Tel: 01588 650656
mickandgill@btconnect.com
Ratlinghope, Shrewsbury, Shropshire, SY5 0SP

DETAILS
■ **Open** - All year. Arrive after 4pm and leave before 10.30am.
■ **Beds** - 10: 2x4, 1x2
■ **Price/night** - £250 for up to 10 people. Min stay 2 nights. £1 pppn discount if arriving without a vehicle. Dogs welcome and free.

CONTACT: Frankie Goode; Mike Goode
Tel: 01694 722593 or 07870 147123
info@allstrettonbunkhouse.co.uk
www.allstrettonbunkhouse.co.uk
Meadow Green, Batch Valley, All Stretton, Shrops, SY6 6JW

STOKES BARN
BUNKHOUSES
41a

On top of Wenlock Edge AONB in the heart of Shropshire, Stokes Barn has two bunkhouses with comfortable, centrally heated, dormitory accommodation. Perfect for corporate groups, walkers, field study, schools, stag/hen parties or reunions with friends/family. Ironbridge World Heritage Site is 6 miles away. Much Wenlock is within walking distance with shops, pubs & sports facilities.

 GROUPS ONLY

DETAILS
- **Open** - All year. All day.
- **Beds** - Threshing Barn 28: 1x12,1x10,1x6 Granary 16: 1x10,1x4,1x2
- **Price/night** - Prices per min 2 nights: Barn: £560 midweek, £910 weekend. Granary: £398 midweek, £615 weekend. Both units weekend 2 nights: £1365.

CONTACT: Helen
Tel: 01952 727491
info@stokesbarn.co.uk
www.stokesbarn.co.uk
Stokes Barn, Newtown Farm, Much Wenlock, Shropshire, TF13 6DB

SPRINGHILL
FARM BUNKHOUSE
41b

Part of a Welsh hill farm on the Wales/ Shropshire border at 1475ft above sea level, with beautiful views over the Ceiriog Valley and Berwyn Mountains. Great for walking, riding, cycling, team building, meetings, or just to relax . The bunkhouse has under-floor heating, entrance hall, drying room, large self catering kitchen, dining area & lounge. The patio and lawn have a BBQ and hot tub. Horse riding and archery on site. Good walking from the door. Horses and pets on request. Limited WiFi & mobile.

DETAILS
- **Open** - All year by arrangement.
- **Beds** - Bunkhouse: 25, Cottages: 2x6
- **Price/night** - £25pp. (including bedding but not towels).

CONTACT: Sue Benbow
Tel: 01691 718406
sue@springhillfarm.co.uk
springhill.farm
Springhill Farm, Glyn Ceiriog, Selattyn, Oswestry, Shropshire, SY10 7NZ

BUNKHOUSE
AT THE WORKHOUSE
42a

ACKERS
ADVENTURE
42b

The well equipped, community run bunkhouse at Y Dolydd Llanfyllin Workhouse is handy for Welshpool & Shrewsbury and close to the Berwyn Mountains. With access to a wide range of adventurous activities including Lake Vyrnwy, Pistyll Rhaeadr waterfall (the tallest in the UK) and Revolution bike park. Venue hire for events welcomed.

Visit the free History Centre to learn more about the building and the people who lived and worked in it.

DETAILS
- **Open** - All year.
- **Beds** - 24: 1x4, 1x8, 1x12
- **Price/night** - From £16pp incl. linen, duvets & pillow. Group discounts may apply.

CONTACT: Debbie Hicks
Tel: 01691 649 062
jean.workhouse@gmail.com
www.the-workhouse.org.uk Y Dolydd, Workhouse, Llanfyllin, SY22 5LD

Ackers Residential Centre (ARC) is a purpose built accommodation centre set in 70 acres of semi rural land just 2 miles from the centre of Birmingham. Perfect for The Sea Life Centre, Cadbury World, Thinktank, The Bull Ring shopping centre, National Motorcycle Museum & the NEC. With 9 sleeping rooms, a fully equipped self-catering kitchen, dining area and a rec room with TV, DVD, games and comfy seating. Ackers Adventure provide instructor led outdoor activities on site which can be incorporated into your stay.

 GROUPS ONLY

DETAILS
- **Open** - All year.
- **Beds** - 26: 4x4, 5x2
- **Price/night** - Enquire for price.

CONTACT: Laura Macbeath
Tel: 0121 772 5111
bookings@ackers-adventure.co.uk
www.ackers-adventure.co.uk
Ackers (ARC), Waverley Canal Basin, Small Heath, Birmingham, B10 0DQ

BELL HEATH
CENTRE
43a

VIKING
CENTRE
43b

Bell Heath Centre, set amidst 20 acres of secluded woodlands, offers the perfect rural escape with excellent transport links to Birmingham. The centre sleeps up to 92 and outdoor adventures can be organised on site. This spacious centre is perfect for large family gatherings, reunions, weddings, stag/hen parties, schools, faith groups & corporate events. Facilities include a commercial kitchen, a hall (seating 100), lounge & games room.

Situated in the village of Claxby in the Lincolnshire Wolds Area of Outstanding Natural Beauty, this low cost hostel has a well equipped kitchen and good sized communal area. Within easy reach of Lincoln, Gainsborough, Scunthorpe and Grimsby. The perfect location for: walking, cycling, field studies, outdoor pursuits, educational activities and conservation projects. Popular with family groups, schools, scouts, guides, walkers, cycling groups and other organisations.

DETAILS

- **Open** - All year
- **Beds** - 92: Main Centre: 78: 9x8, 3x2. Cottage: 8. Snug: 6 + glamping/campsite
- **Price/night** - From £27.50pp with a minium group size. Please enquire for holiday cottages, glamping and campsite.

CONTACT: Reception
Tel: 01684 574546
enquiries@boundlessoutdoors.co.uk
boundlessevents.co.uk
Quantry Lane, Belbroughton,
Stourbridge, Worcestershire. DY9 9UU

DETAILS

- **Open** - Open
- **Beds** - 20: 2x4, 2x6
- **Price/night** - £120 for 1st night, £110 for subsequent nights.

CONTACT: Susannah Boulton
Tel: 07903 584114
info@thevikingcentre.com
www.thevikingcentre.com
Pelham Road, Claxby, Market Rasen,
Lincolnshire LN8 3YR

HULL TRINITY
BACKPACKERS
44a

IGLOO
HYBRID
44b

In the heart of historic Hull this hostel is aimed at the individual traveller, groups, cyclists and families. Perfect for visiting Hull's museums & attractions, such as The Deep, Marina, theatres and Bonus Arena. Sport fans friendly too. Family en-suite, singles and dorms. Self-catering kitchenettte and coffee lounge. Ideal for visiting the East Yorkshire Coast, historic Beverley and York. Daily ferries to the Netherlands.

Off Market Square, right in the centre of Nottingham, Igloo Hybrid offers great value and comfort. With dorms, singles, doubles, triples, and family quarters as well as our posh en-suite Shed digs. Rooms and communal areas feature up-cycled furniture and street art murals, with a self-catering kitchen, WiFi, power showers, lockers, lounge & courtyard.

DETAILS

- **Open** - All year. All day. Reception open 7am-1am Sun-Fri, 24hrs Sat.
- **Beds** - 58: dorms, singles, twins, doubles, triples, quads and family rooms.
- **Price/night** - Dorms: from £24pp. Sleep pods, singles & doubles from £36. Triples from £54. Family rooms from £70. Ensuites from £44.

DETAILS

- **Open** - All year (not Xmas & New Year). 5-10pm check in, flexible with notice.
- **Beds** - 20+: 1x6, 2x4, 1x family en-suite, 3 x single/twin. Flexible.
- **Price/night** - £19pp (dorm), £32pp (single). £39 (twin). En-suite £49.

CONTACT: Glenn Gavin
Tel: 07853 000474 or 01482 223229
hulltrinitybackpackers@gmail.com
hulltrinitybackpackers.com
51/52 Market Place, Kingston Upon Hull.
HU1 1RQ

CONTACT: Igloo Hybrid
Tel: 0115 9483822
hybrid@igloohostel.co.uk
www.igloohostel.co.uk
4-6 Eldon Chambers, Wheeler Gate,
Nottingham, NG1 2NS

SHINING CLIFF
HOSTEL
45a

With its own crags, streams, lakes & 600-acres of mature woodland, Shining Cliff Hostel has nature on its doorstep. Access is half a mile from the nearest parking area along a woodland footpath. Paths lead through the woods to the A6 at Ambergate (20 mins' walk) which has a food shop, pub, buses and trains to Derby. The hostel is ideal for a wide range of groups wishing to enjoy time away in a peaceful woodland setting.

DETAILS

- **Open** - All year.
- **Beds** - 20: 1x4, 2x6, 2x2
- **Price/night** - Sole use: £320 Fri/Sat (min 2 nights). £120-£250 Sun-Thur (depending on group size). Room bookings: 2 beds £30, 4 beds £60, 6 beds £90 (Sun-Thurs only)

CONTACT: Kate Tuck
Tel: 07794 268059
shiningcliffhostel@yahoo.com
shiningcliffhostel.co.uk
Alderwasley, Derbyshire. DE56 2RE

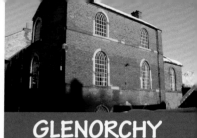

GLENORCHY
CENTRE
45b

The Glenorchy Centre is on the edge of the Peak District National Park in the historic market town of Wirksworth. Close by are the High Peak Trail for walking & cycling, and Black Rocks for bouldering & climbing. Nearby Cromford has Arkwright's mills, a World Heritage Site, & Cromford Canal. Suitable for self-catering groups, the accommodation includes a spacious multi-purpose hall.

      GROUPS ONLY

DETAILS

- **Open** - March to November
- **Beds** - 26: 1x12, 1x8, 1x4, 1x2
- **Price/night** - 2 nights (minimum stay) £985 plus each subsequent night £325. Small groups £30 per person per night with a minimum charge of £650 for a 2 night stay.

CONTACT: The Secretary
Tel: 01629 824323
secretary@glenorchycentre.org.uk
www.glenorchycentre.org.uk
Chapel Lane, Wirksworth, Derbyshire, DE4 4FF

MOUNT COOK
ADVENTURE CENTRE
46a

ASHBOURNE
GATEWAY CENTRE
46b

Mount Cook, a fantastic purpose built centre, offers groups of 8 - 180 the perfect base for an exciting weekend or holiday in the Peak District. A whole range of outside activities can be organised on- or off site for a min of 8 people. Popular with schools, clubs, corporate team building, weddings and gatherings of friends and families. B&B, full or half board. Self catering with sole use bookings.

Ashbourne Gateway Centre, in the pretty market town of Ashbourne, provides groups of up to 27 with a perfect base for exploring the landscape & attractions of the Peak District. It is popular with schools, uniformed & youth groups, gatherings of friends/families and groups of walkers/cyclists. The Tissington trail off-road cycle/walking route starts opposite. Carsington Water, The Roaches & Alton Towers make great days out and are all close by.

     GROUPS ONLY

      GROUPS ONLY

DETAILS
■ **Open** - All year. Office hours; weekdays 9-5.
■ **Beds** - 180: 140 Beds: 34x4 + 2x2 (disabled access), 10 Pods: 10x4 + 40 Camping
■ **Price/night** - Contact Mount Cook.

DETAILS
■ **Open** - All year
■ **Beds** - 27: 1x12, 3x4, 1x2, 1x1
■ **Price/night** - £18pp (min £220pn, max £440pn). Min stay 2 nights. 50% rate reduction for nights 3 to 7.

CONTACT: The Office
Tel: 01629 823 702
Explore@mountcook.uk
www.mountcook.uk
Porter Lane, Middleton-by-Wirksworth, Matlock, DE4 4LS

CONTACT: Anne
Tel: 07849 771827
ashbourne.gateway@gmail.com
ashbournegateway.org.uk
Ashbourne Methodist Church, Church Street, Ashbourne, Derbyshire DE6 1AE

ALSTONEFIELD
CAMPING BARN
47a

BUTTERTON
CAMPING BARNS
47b

Close to Dovedale, the Manifold Cycle Trail, Carsington Water, Alton Towers & the Roaches Rocks (great for climbers). Ideal for quiet group get-togethers, families, cyclists, walkers, DofE, scouts, schools and team building. Camping in the comfort of a remote cosy barn with log burning stove, toilet & water. No electric and no distractions. Stands in a meadow, off the beaten track with great views. BYO camping equipment.

Fenns Farm Accommodation can offer guests accommodation to suit all budgets. It consists of four properties, Waterslacks Camping Barn sleeping 15, Wills 'Glamping' Barn sleeping 6 and two holiday cottages, Fenns & Foggs Barn both sleeping 7. All the accommodation is situated on the edge of the Peak District village of Butterton, in walking distance of the local pub and the Manifold Valley.

DETAILS

- **Open** - All year. All day apart from Christmas and New Year.
- **Beds** - 12: BYO sleeping mats & bags
- **Price/night** - £132. Discounts mid-week outside of school hols when made by email directly from this website.

CONTACT: Robert or Teresa Flower
Tel: 01335 310349
gateham.grange@btinternet.com
www.gatehamgrange.co.uk
Gateham Grange, Alstonefield,
Ashbourne, Derbys. DE6 2FT

DETAILS

- **Open** - All year. All day
- **Beds** - 35: Waterslacks:15. Wills:6. Fenns:7. Foggs:7
- **Price/night** - Waterslacks from £155, Wills from £85, Fenns Barn and Foggs Barn from £200.

CONTACT: Jason and Michelle
Tel: 07376 489047 or 07708 200282
fennsfarmaccommodation@gmail.com
www.peakdistrictbarns.co.uk/
Fenns Farm, Wetton Road, Butterton,
Leek, Staffordshire, ST13 7ST

SHEEN
BUNKHOUSE
48a

ROACHES
BUNKHOUSE
48b

Sheen Bunkhouse is in a quiet corner of the Peak District, close to the beautiful Dove and Manifold valleys. It has a well equipped self-catering kitchen, lounge, two bunkrooms and separate toilets & showers.

The Manifold Track, Tissington Trail and High Peak Trail give easy access to beautiful countryside, ideal for families and cyclists. Dovedale and the moors offer stunning walking. Buxton, Leek and Bakewell are within 12 miles and Alton Towers is 20 minutes away by car.

The Roaches Bunkhouse provides group accommodation at the foot of The Roaches gritstone edge in the Peak District. The area has some of the best climbing in the country plus walks & cycling in stunning scenery. Facilities include a large communal area with tables & chairs, a log fire, DVDs & board games. There's a small well equipped kitchen. Outside there's a BBQ area and on-site parking. Walking distance to Ye Old Rock Inn & the Roaches Tearooms. 3 miles to the bustling market town of Leek.

DETAILS

- **Open** - All year. 24 hours access. Reception 8am - 9pm.
- **Beds** - 14: 1x8, 1x6
- **Price/night** - From: Adults £20, u16 £15.

CONTACT: Jean or Graham Belfield
Tel: 01298 84501 or 7538932708
grahambelfield11@gmail.com
Peakstones, Sheen, Derbys, SK17 0ES

DETAILS

- **Open** - All year.
- **Beds** - 36: 3x2, 4x4, 1x6, 1x 8 bed
- **Price/night** - Sole use from £500.

CONTACT: Emma Baines
Tel: 01538 300308
info@roachesbunkhouse.com
www.roachesbunkhouse.com
Upper Hulme Mill, Roach Road, Upper Hulme, Nr Leek, Staffordshire, ST13 8TY

THE RECKONING
HOUSE

49a

Renovated to a high standard including double glazing and insulation, the Reckoning House is situated 3 miles from Bakewell. It is on the edge of the Lathkill Dale National Nature Reserve, full of interesting flora and fauna as well as outstanding geological features.

Horse riding, fishing, golf and cycle hire are available locally. Local walks include the Limestone Way. Facilities include: cooking area, 4 calor gas rings (gas supplied), hot water for washing up & showers, storage heaters in all rooms.

      GROUPS ONLY

DETAILS
- **Open** - All year. By arrangement.
- **Beds** - 12: 2x6 bunk rooms.
- **Price/night** - Sole use £120 per night

CONTACT: Rachel Rhodes
Tel: 01629 812416 or 7960169777
mandalecampsite@yahoo.co.uk
www.mandalecampsite.co.uk
Mandale Farm, Haddon Grove,
Bakewell, Derbyshire, DE45 1JF

THORNBRIDGE
OUTDOORS

49b

Thornbridge Outdoors offers excellent flexible group accommodation. With its superb location in the heart of the Peak District you have access to wonderful countryside, quaint villages, stately homes, and the traffic free Monsal Trail, popular with walkers and cyclists.

    **GROUPS ONLY**

DETAILS
- **Open** - All year.
- **Beds** - 86 in accommodation. 40 in teepees, plus camping. Lodge 38: 4x5, 4x3, 1x6. Farm House 38: 2x8, 2x6, 1x5, 1x3, 1x2. Woodlands 10: 1x5, 1x4, 1x1. Teepees 40: 9x4/5. Plus camping.
- **Price/night** - W/end: 2 nights: £1324 (Farm House) & £1656.20 (Lodge). W/end: 3 nights £661.50 (Woodlands). Ask for weekdays, longer stays & activities.

CONTACT: Customer Services and Business Support Team
Tel: 01629 640491
thornbridgeoutdoors@sheffield.gov.uk
www.thornbridgeoutdoors.co.uk
Great Longstone, Bakewell, DE45 1NY

BRETTON
HOSTEL
50a

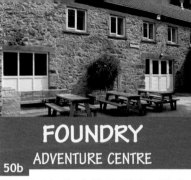

FOUNDRY
ADVENTURE CENTRE
50b

Bretton Hostel, in the heart of the Peak District near Eyam & Hathersage, feels remote on Bretton Edge. It is a peaceful space with far-reaching views across the Peak. Excellent walks & cycle rides from the door. Perfect for winding down, for outdoor activities & for gatherings. Fully equipped kitchen, living/dining room, WiFi, secure cycle store and eco-studio. Bottom sheet provided, but bring your own bedding. Local pubs nearby.

With all of the Peak District National Park within easy access, the centre is an ideal location for activities and tourism and it welcomes a wide range of groups. 31 or 52 bed configurations can be booked.

The spacious centre includes; a large lounge with library, TV and wood burning stove, well equipped kitchens & dining areas. An extensive network of paths give access to the countryside. Adventure activities available, great for team building & courses.

DETAILS

- **Open** - Sole use all year. Beds/rooms May-Sept (Mon-Thu only). Arrive from 4pm, depart by 11am.
- **Beds** - 17: 1x8, 1x6, 1x3
- **Price/night** - Sole use from £302 (min 2 nights), large groups & weekends more. Beds £28, private rooms from £55.

CONTACT: Clare Palmer
Tel: 07792 385134
bookings@brettonhostel.co.uk
brettonhostel.co.uk
Bretton, Eyam, Hope Valley, S32 5QD

DETAILS

- **Open** - All year. All day.
- **Beds** - 52 or 31 in 9 bedrooms
- **Price/night** - 31 beds from £780 per night, 52 beds from £1080 per night.

CONTACT: Tim Gould
Tel: 07786 332702
tim@foundrymountain.co.uk
foundryadventurecentre.co.uk
The Old Playhouse, Great Hucklow, Derbyshire, SK17 8RF

PINDALE
OUTDOOR CENTRE
51a

51b

BRADWELL
WAR MEMORIAL HALL

A mile from Castleton in the Peak District, Pindale Farm offers a range of accommodation: B&B in the farmhouse. Six self-catering/self-contained rooms sleeping 8 or 10 people in the Barn. A self-catering unit sleeping 8 people in The Engine House. Plus an AA 3 Pennant campsite. Perfect for D of E expeditions and many outdoor activities. Instruction is available.

Bradwell War Memorial Hall is in the pretty village of Bradwell in the heart of the Peak District. This community run hall offers low cost self-catering accommodation to groups of 6-42.

An ideal base for walkers, bikers, DofE students or climbers who wish to explore this popular area. There are no beds so BYO sleeping mat and bedding. The rooms are centrally heated, there's a well equipped kitchen & hot showers.

DETAILS
- **Open** - All year (camping March-October). 24 hours.
- **Beds** - 64: Farmhouse: 4. Engine House: 8. Barn: 52: 4x8, 2x10. + camping.
- **Price/night** - Camping £10pp, hook up £6, gazebo £10. DofE discount £1pp. Barns £20pp + £1 electric tokens.

CONTACT: Alan Medhurst
Tel: 01433 620111
info@pindalefarm.co.uk
www.pindalefarm.co.uk
Pindale Road, Hope, Hope Valley, Derbyshire, S33 6RN

GROUPS ONLY

DETAILS
- **Open** - Weekends and school holidays only.
- **Beds** - 42: 1x30, 1x6, 1x4/6
- **Price/night** - £150 per night, weekends & school holidays only. PLEASE NOTE there are no beds. BYO sleeping mat and bedding

CONTACT: Esther Gillott
bradwellwarmemorial@gmail.com
Netherside, Bradwell, Hope Valley, Derbyshire S33 9HJ

ST MICHAELS
CENTRE
52a

St Michael's Centre, located in the village of Hathersage, provides high quality family friendly group accommodation, surrounded by the beautiful countryside of the Peak District National Park. There are comfortable dormitory style bunk beds and a lovely central hall which provides a fantastic communal kitchen, dining and lounge area for enjoyable shared living. Attached cottage also available separately or for larger groups.

DETAILS

■ **Open** - All year. Office open Monday to Friday 8.30 am - 4pm
■ **Beds** - 38: 2x2, 1x4, 2x6, 1x8, 1x10. Plus 4/6 in attached cottage.
■ **Price/night** - From £550 per night for 20 people, plus £25 per additional person. Min stay 2 nights. Short notice discounts.

CONTACT: Centre Office
Tel: 01433 650309
stmichaels@nottscc.gov.uk
nottsoutdoors.nottinghamshire.gov.uk
Main Road, Hathersage, S32 1BB

THORPE FARM
BUNKHOUSES
52b

Close to Hathersage and 2 miles west of Stanage Edge, the bunkhouses are on a family-run dairy farm. Popular areas for climbing, walking from meadows to moorland with fantastic views & mountain biking. Each bunkhouse is heated and has a living room, kitchen, bathrooms with toilets, showers and washbasins. Sleep in dorms with bunks or the Hayloft has mattresses on the gallery floor. Camping is available. Secure bike storage and free parking.

DETAILS

■ **Open** - All year. No restrictions.
■ **Beds** - 78: Old Shippon 32: 2x12, 2x4. Old Stables 14: 1x8, 1x6. Pondside 14: 1x8, 1x6. Byre 14: 1x6, 1x4. Hayloft: 4
■ **Price/night** - See own website.

CONTACT: Jane Marsden
Tel: 01433 650659
jane@hope-valley.co.uk
www.thorpe-bunk.co.uk
Thorpe Farm, Hathersage, Peak District, Via Sheffield, S32 1BQ

HOMESTEAD
& CHEESEHOUSE
53a

53b
EDALE BARN
COTEFIELD FARM

In the heart of Bamford these two bunkhouses are on a small farm just 3 miles from the iconic Stanage Edge.

Perfectly located for visiting Castleton, Chatsworth House & Hathersage. Both bunkhouses are centrally heated with hot showers & well equipped kitchens. Sheets & pillows are provided. BYO sleeping bags.

Overlooking Mam Tor, at the start of the Pennine Way, Edale Barn is a traditional camping barn; a stone tent with a wooden sleeping platform. Close to Kinder Scout, Jacobs Ladder, Kinder Downfall & Hollins Cross. Adjoining the barn, but with external access, is a cooking area with a mains water tap and a chemical toilet. There is no heating or electricity. BYO sleeping mats/bags, cooking equipment and torches. Pubs serving meals are an easy walk away.

DETAILS
- **Open** - All year. Check in after 4pm. Check out by 11am.
- **Beds** - 26: Homestead 22: 1x10, 2x6. Cheesehouse 4: 1x4
- **Price/night** - From £17.50pp. Sole use: Homestead £230, Cheesehouse £50. Min 2 nights for Homestead at weekends. Phone for a quote for single night.

CONTACT: Helena Platts
Tel: 01433 651298
The Farm, Bamford, Hope Valley
S33 0BL

DETAILS
- **Open** - All year. Arrive after 4pm and depart before 10am.
- **Beds** - 8 on platform + 6 camping
- **Price/night** - £9 per person. £72 sole use per night

CONTACT: Sally Gee
Tel: 01433 670273 or 07507 405161
sallygee52@hotmail.com
www.fb.com/cotefieldfarmcottages
Cotefield Farm, Olllerbrook, Edale, Hope Valley, Derbyshire. S33 7ZG

OLLERBROOK
FARM BUNKHOUSES 54a

Close to the start of the Pennine Way with easy access to Kinder Scout and the village of Edale via a network of footpaths from the doorstep. Castleton, Buxton, Bakewell and Chatsworth House are all within 40 minutes' drive. There are 2 bunkhouses each with a fully equipped kitchen and available for sole use by groups. Bring your own sleeping bags and personal towels.

DETAILS

- **Open** - All year. All day. Arrive after 4pm depart before 10.30am.
- **Beds** - Nab View 18: 3x6, Stables Bunkhouse 14: 3x4,1x2
- **Price/night** - Nab View: £720 (2 nights). Stables Bunkhouse: £480 (2 nights), midweek enquire for 2 night stays.

CONTACT: Sheila
Tel: 01433 670235
ollerbrookfarm@gmail.com
www.ollerbrookfarm.co.uk
Ollerbrook Booth, Edale, Hope Valley,
Derbyshire, S33 7ZG

JOHN HUNT
BASE 54b

The John Hunt Base is situated in the High Peak on the site of Hagg Farm.

The base offers comfortable, family friendly accommodation ideal for sightseeing, hill walking, trail running and biking as well as quieter pursuits such as photography. There is a picnic area, wildlife garden with fire pit and a playing field with climbing boulder. Activities can be arranged including climbing, stream scrambling, caving & on-site high ropes.

DETAILS

- **Open** - All year. Office: Mon-Thur 8.30am- 4.30pm, Fri 8.30-3.30pm
- **Beds** - 18: 1x8, 1x6, 2x2.
- **Price/night** - £250 per night, minimum booking two nights.

CONTACT:
Tel: 01433 651594
haggfarm@nottscc.gov.uk
nottsoutdoors.nottinghamshire.gov.uk
Hagg Farm OEC, Snake Rd, Bamford,
Hope Valley, S33 0BJ

HAGG FARM
OUTDOOR CENTRE
55a

LOCKERBROOK FARM
OUTDOOR CENTRE
55b

Situated in the Peak District's Woodlands Valley, Hagg Farm offers comfortable accommodation for up to 44 people with an additional 18 beds in the John Hunt Base next door (also in this Guide). Part of Nottinghamshire C.C's Environmental & Outdoor Education Service, Hagg Farm is available for private hire by groups, families, clubs & charitable organisations. It can be booked on a self-catering or catered basis.

Lockerbrook Farm Outdoor Centre, operated by The Woodcraft Folk, is situated in glorious isolation high above Ladybower Reservoir. The Centre has stunning views across the Upper Derwent Valley. The converted hill farm provides accommodation in two units; the Cottage sleeps 6 and the Bunk Barn 38. Catering & outdoor activities available with notice.

DETAILS

- **Open** - All year. Office: Mon-Thurs 8:30am-4.30pm, Fri 8:30am-4pm
- **Beds** - 44: 4x8, 2x4, 2x2
- **Price/night** - £24pp: min charge for 25 people, min 2 night stay. Outdoor activity instruction for 12 from £300 per day.

DETAILS

- **Open** - All year.
- **Beds** - 44: Bunk Barn: 38 (36 in bunks + 2 fold-out beds). Cottage 6: (2 x twin, 1 x dbl).
- **Price/night** - Bunk Barn: £890 - £1102. Cottage: £324- £444 for 2 nights. Discount for schools and youth groups.

CONTACT: Kirsty Weatherall
Tel: 01433 651594
haggfarm@nottscc.gov.uk
nottsoutdoors.nottinghamshire.gov.uk
Hagg Farm OEC, Snake Rd, Bamford, Hope Valley, S33 0BJ

CONTACT: Jo Holliday or Matt North
Tel: 01433 651412
lockerbrook@woodcraft.org.uk
lockerbrook.org.uk
Snake Pass, Bamford, Hope Valley, Derbyshire, S33 0BJ

BOARSHURST CENTRE
SADDLEWORTH
56a

The Boarshurst Centre is situated on the north western edge of the Peak District yet with easy road and rail links to Manchester (12 miles away).

With 32 beds across 2 dorms and 2 leaders' rooms the centre provides well appointed self catering accommodation for child, youth, adult and family/friend groups who seek to practice outdoor pursuits. BYO sleeping bags

 GROUPS ONLY

DETAILS
- **Open** - All year. Check in from 12 noon or earlier by arrangement.
- **Beds** - 32: 2x12, 2x4
- **Price/night** - Sole Use. Adult Groups: £500. Family Groups £450. Child/Youth Groups £400.

CONTACT: Mark Jones
Tel: 07979 864472
theboarshurstcentre@gmail.com
www.boarshurstcentre.org
Boarshurst Lane, Greenfield, Oldham
OL3 7EA

EMBASSIE
BACKPACKERS
56b

The Embassie is a majestic terraced house in an unspoilt Georgian square. Until 1986 it was the Consulate of Venezuela! Only 15 minutes' walk from the centre of Liverpool, known for its nightlife, it's in the perfect position. Recently refurbished, there are new kitchen facilities, a brand new shower suite and an all new games room & relax area with Sky Sports and HD television. The hostel is clean, safe and staffed 24 hours. Bedding is provided (including sheets) and free coffee, tea, toast and jam are available 24 hours.

DETAILS
- **Open** - All year. All day.
- **Beds** - 50
- **Price/night** - £19 (Sunday to Thursday), £25 Friday, £32 Saturday

CONTACT: Kevin
Tel: 0151 707 1089
embassie@gmail.com
www.embassie.com
1 Falkner Square, Liverpool, L8 7NU

HEBDEN BRIDGE
HOSTEL
57a

The recently refurbished Hebden Bridge Hostel, run by national arts organisation IOU, offers contemporary, comfortable & affordable accommodation at the heart of this vibrant independent town.

Exclusive use, dorms and private rooms are available, all with ensuite facilities. Perfect for solo travellers, families or groups. Everyone is welcome.

DETAILS
- **Open** - All year
- **Beds** - 45: 1x3 (dbl + sgl), 9x4 (all sgl), 1x6 (bunks)
- **Price/night** - Dorm bed £25. 6 bed room £100/£120. Quad £80/£100. Triple £70/£85, Twin £60/£80, Single £40/£60. Exclusive use from £600 to £900.

CONTACT: Jill
Tel: 01422 553578
bookings@hebdenbridgehostel.org
hebdenbridgehostel.org
The Birchcliffe Centre, Hebden Bridge, W Yorks, HX7 8DG

HEIGHT GATE
57b

Bunkhouse accommodation for groups of 32 in a 17th-century stone farmhouse high above the Calder Valley. Facilities include a well-appointed kitchen, large communal lounge and indoor barn for activities. Outside you'll find a BBQ, fire pit, campfire area, a field for games and overflow camping and parking for 8 cars. BYO bedding and towels.

   **GROUPS ONLY**

DETAILS
- **Open** - All year: Check in from 2pm. Check out by 12.
- **Beds** - 32: 1x2, 1x8, 1x10, 1x12 plus camping
- **Price/night** - Sole use from: £246 (winter/spring/autumn), £321-£385 (summer). Enquire for mid-week discounts.

CONTACT: Andy Worster
Tel: 020 3890 1963
heightgate@woodcraft.org.uk
www.heightgate.org.uk
Dyke Lane, Todmorden, West Yorkshire, OL14 6DL.

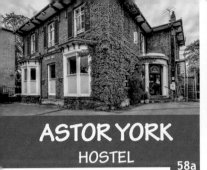

ASTOR YORK
HOSTEL
58a

Astor York is set in a beautiful Grade II listed building just minutes' walk to the historic centre!

With a huge cosy lounge & dining areas, free WiFi throughout the building and every room en suite, Astor York is the perfect base for exploring the incredible historic centre of York. There is also a bar on the property if you fancy a drink with friends, or to meet fellow travellers, and a kitchen where you can cook your own food if you are on a budget!

DETAILS
- **Open** - All year
- **Beds** - 93: 1x1, 1x twin, 2x dbl. 9x4, 2x6, 1x8, 1x12, 1x18
- **Price/night** - Dorm beds from £17pp. Private double/twin from £58.

CONTACT: Eric
Tel: 01904 653 786
eric@astorhostels.com
astorhostels.com/hostels/york
124 Holgate Road, York, YO24 4BB

STABLESIDE
YORK
58b

Stableside, a quiet & welcoming 4* hostel situated right on the historic Knavesmire, is the perfect location for enjoying a break in the city of York. Guests can take advantage of the varied room options catering for the single traveller and larger groups. Free parking, free WiFi, function room and a fabulous Yorkshire welcome. Meals can be provided for groups. On the NCN Route 65 for easy access to the city centre.

DETAILS
- **Open** - All year (except during race meetings). All day.
- **Beds** - 100: 2x6, 21x4, 8 x triple, 1 x twin, 11 x single.
- **Price/night** - B&B twin room £90 inc towels. Enquire for group rates.

CONTACT: Fay
Tel: 01904 709174
fay.waudby@yorkracecourse.co.uk
www.stablesideyork.co.uk
Stableside, York Racing Stables, York, YO24 1QG

SCARBOROUGH
YOUTH HOSTEL
59a

For a fun filled, seaside break Scarborough is unbeatable: two safe, sandy beaches, penny arcades, pirate ship, three surf schools and the Alpamare Waterpark. Once a 17th century water mill on a quiet riverside just outside the town, Scarborough Youth Hostel is also a perfect base for exploring the coast and country of the North York Moors and Wolds with miles of paths, tracks and quiet lanes for walkers and cyclists.

DETAILS
- **Open** - Seasonal. 8-10am & 5-10pm. Group arrival time by arrangement.
- **Beds** - 42: Main House 22: 2x6, 1x5, 1x4, 1x2 . Annexe 20: in 4 rooms.
- **Price/night** - Please enquire for prices.

CONTACT: Robert Fletcher
Tel: 01723 448900
scarboroughhostel@gmail.com
www.yha.org.uk
The White House, Burniston Road, Scarborough, YO13 0DA

THE OLD SCHOOL
HOUSE
59b

The Old School House welcomes schools, groups, walkers and families to the picturesque village of Robins Hood's Bay. Home to one of the best beaches on Yorkshire's east coast. At the end of Wainright's Coast to Coast walk and on The Cleveland Way. Ideal for groups of families and friends to book exclusively and also available to individual families looking for an affordable holiday by the sea.

DETAILS
- **Open** - All year
- **Beds** - 41: 6x4, 3x6
- **Price/night** - Sole use: £400-£550. Self-catering 4 bed family room: £60, six bed: £70. School packages from £37.50 to £40 per child.

CONTACT: Helen & Dave
Tel: 01947 880723 or 07754 168178
dave@oldschoolhouserhb.co.uk
www.oldschoolhouserhb.co.uk
Fisherhead, Robin Hoods Bay, Whitby, Yorkshire. YO22 4ST

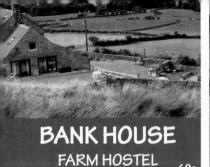

BANK HOUSE
FARM HOSTEL
60a

Luxury bunkbarn, camping barn and B&B on an organic farm in beautiful Glaisdale Dale. Stunning views of the North York Moors and just 1 mile from the Coast to Coast route.

The bunkbarn is warm & well appointed with one dorm of mostly single beds. The camping barn provides simple, single-night shelter for walkers and cyclists.

DETAILS
- **Open** - All year. Phone calls 9am-9pm.
- **Beds** - 18: Bunkbarn: 10: 8x singles, 1x bunk. Camping barn: 8: 2x4
- **Price/night** - Bunkbarn: W/ends £600 (2 nights), midweek £30pppn (min 2 people, 2 nights). Sat £400. Camping Barn: £12pp. Farmhouse B&B: £40pp.

CONTACT: Chris or Emma Padmore
Tel: 01947 897297
info@bankhousefarmhostel.co.uk
www.bankhousefarmhostel.co.uk
Bank House Farm, Glaisdale, Whitby
YO21 2QA

YORKSHIRE
CYCLE HUB
60b

The perfect bunkhouse for cyclists, walkers and lovers of the outdoors.This stylish purpose-built bunk house has a bike shop, repair centre, cafe & bike hire.

Situated away from the crowds in the stunningly beautiful North York Moors National Park, the Yorkshire Cyclehub Bunkhouse sleeps up to 26 guests across 6 ensuite rooms.

Book by the bed, the room or book sole use of the whole place.

DETAILS
- **Open** - All year.
- **Beds** - 26: 2x3, 2x4, 2x6
- **Price/night** - From £35pp. Sole Use £850.

CONTACT: Ann or Philip
Tel: 01287 669098
stay@yorkshirecyclehub.co.uk
www.yorkshirecyclehub.uk
Fryup Gill Farm, Great Fryup Dale,
Whitby, North Yorkshire Y021 2AP

COTE GHYLL
MILL
61a

BROMPTON ON SWALE
BUNKBARN
61b

Situated in a beautiful secluded valley in the NY Moors National Park, this refurbished mill with en suite rooms, is perfect for those wishing to explore the Yorkshire moors, dales & coast. You can book the whole Mill, a room or a bed. Great for educational groups, families, outdoor clubs and gatherings of friends. Group activities and catering available. Next to Cod Beck reservoir, Cleveland Way, Coast to Coast & Lyke Wake Walk.

Located on a small working farm, just 3 miles east of Richmond, Yorkshire. Brompton on Swale Bunkbarn offers a welcome break from walking or cycling the Coast to Coast. A pot of tea for weary walkers upon arrival and safe storage for bikes makes this bunkhouse especially welcoming. Close to the Yorkshire Dales, Swaledale, Wensleydale, Easby Abbey, Richmond Castle & Ellerton Lakes.

Dogs welcome (on a lead as there are ducks, hens and geese.)

DETAILS
- **Open** - All year. 7am - 9pm
- **Beds** - 61: Mill 61: 4x2, 6x4, 4x6 + 5 rollout beds
- **Price/night** - Adults from £32. Family rooms from £57. Enquire for groups & sole use.

DETAILS
- **Open** - All year. All day
- **Beds** - 12: 3x4
- **Price/night** - £15 per person. Sole use £180. Sleeping bag hire £2, towels £1. Electricity meter £1.

CONTACT: Reception
Tel: 01609 883425
mill@coteghyll.com
www.coteghyll.com
Osmotherley, Northallerton, North Yorkshire, DL6 3AH

CONTACT: Chris Wilkin
Tel: 01748 818326
chris01748@gmail.com
24 Richmond Road, Richmond, North Yorkshire, DL10 7HE

EARBY
HOSTEL

DALE HOUSE
BARN

Cosy, historic hostel with large kitchen & dining room which can seat all 21 people in one room. Lounge with log burner.

Secure cycle storage for 20 bikes. Large wildlife garden with BBQ. Private parking for 6 cars. Great local pub. Medium sized Co-op supermarket open 7 days 6am to 10pm. Food available with prior request. Good public transport links.

DETAILS
- **Open** - All year.
- **Beds** - 26: Hostel 21: 1x2, 2x6, 1x7. Cottage 5: 1xdbl, 1x3
- **Price/night** - £25pp, or £400 for exclusive use of the whole hostel. Adjoining family cottage (sleeps 5), £70 midweek/£75 weekend.

CONTACT: Matt
Tel: 01282 842349 or 07791 903454
matt@earbyhostel.co.uk
earbyhostel.co.uk
9-11 Birch Hall Lane, Earby, Lancashire, BB18 6JX

Dale House Barn is in the heart of Gisburn Forest in the Forest of Bowland AONB. Sympathetically restored it offers simple, practical accommodation for groups of 4-12. Mattresses provided, BYO bedding. Well equipped kitchen. Free WiFi . Close to the Three Peaks, Pendle Hill, Malham Tarn & the Yorkshire Dales. Ideal for walking, climbing, fishing, cycling, family gatherings and activity groups. Meals available. B&B in the adjoining farmhouse.

DETAILS
- **Open** - All year.
- **Beds** - 12: 1x12
- **Price/night** - Sole use: Mid-week: £200. Weekends & Bank Hols: £250 (2 nights min stay).

CONTACT: Dominique Ashford
Tel: 01200 411095 or 07714 092089
ashforddominique1@mac.com
www.dalehousebarn.co.uk
Dalehead Farm, Dalehead, Slaidburn, Clitheroe, Lancashire, BB7 4TS

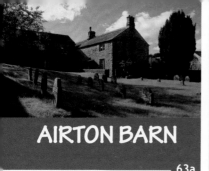

AIRTON BARN

63a

A friendly welcome awaits you Airton Barn.

Next to the 17th century Friends Meeting House. Airton Barn is a simple bunkhouse sleeping up to 12 people, with storage space for 5 bicycles.

On popular walking & cycling routes and surrounded by some of Yorkshire's finest tourist destinations, the Barn is perfect for walkers, cyclists & small group getaways.

DETAILS
- **Open** - Open from April 2023
- **Beds** - 12: 1x6 bunkbeds, 1x6 floor mattresses
- **Price/night** - Please enquire for prices.

CONTACT: Simon Watkins
airtonbarn@gmail.com
airtonbarn.org.uk
The Nook, Airton, Skipton, North Yorkshire, BD23 4AE

WEST END
OUTDOOR CENTRE

63b

Amidst stunning landscape overlooking Thruscross Reservoir on the edge of the Yorkshire Dales National Park, this self-catering centre offers excellent facilities in bunkrooms plus an en suite leader's room. Well equipped kitchen, dining, lounge & shower/toilet areas.

Ideal for team building, youth groups & family parties. 12 miles from Harrogate & Skipton. No stag or hen groups.

DETAILS
- **Open** - All year. Flexible.
- **Beds** - 30: 4x2, 3x4, 1x6, 1x4 en suite
- **Price/night** - Fri or Sat £425, Midweek £300 (min 2 nights). 1 night midweek £425. 4 nights midweek: £1000, 7 nights £1550. Fri+Sat+BH £1275. £5 per dog.

CONTACT: Hedley or Margaret Verity
Tel: 01943 880207
info@westendoutdoorcentre.co.uk
www.westendoutdoorcentre.co.uk
West End, Summerbridge, Harrogate, HG3 4BA

GRASSINGTON
BUNKBARN
64a

With spectacular views of Wharfedale, Grassington Bunkbarn offers comfortable accommodation for individuals and groups. Featuring a well equipped kitchen and a lounge/games area with Freeview TV, WiFi, good mobile signal & a BBQ area. Walking, cycling, climbing, fishing, horse riding, archaeology, bird watching, geology, botany & golf nearby. There's something for everyone.

DETAILS

■ **Open** - All year. Reception 9am - 5pm, Mon - Fri.
■ **Beds** - 34: 2x12, 1x6, 1x4
■ **Price/night** - Sole use: W/E: £1200 (2 ngts). BH: £1450 (3 ngts). Midweek: £510pn. 4 ngts: £1350. 7 ngts: from £2250. Bed £26 (call for availability).

CONTACT: Rhian, Mark or Janet
Tel: 01756 753882
enquiries@grassingtonbunkbarn.co.uk
www.grassingtonbunkbarn.co.uk
Spring Croft, Moor Lane, Grassington, BD23 5BD

WHARFEDALE
LODGE
64b

Nestling in the Yorkshire Dales, Wharfedale Lodge offers luxury, hotel quality, accommodation to groups of 6-20 in 8 comfortable twin rooms and a further 4 bed family room (2 x bunks). Groups of friends, families and business will enjoy the stunning location and the top quality facilities. With the famous Kilnsey Crag close by, the beautiful market town of Skipton a short drive away, the Dales Way on the doorstep and fishing, golf and pony trekking nearby there will be plenty to keep everyone happy.

DETAILS

■ **Open** - All year.
■ **Beds** - 20: 8 x twin, 1 x 4 bed family room.
■ **Price/night** - Weekends (fri/sat) £1450. Midweek from £350 per night.

CONTACT: Matthew Ramsden
Tel: 07719 200933
contact@wharfedalelodge.com
www.wharfedalelodge.com
Kilnsey, North Yorkshire. BD23 5PT

SKIRFARE
BARN
65a

Skirfare Barn, with its stunning backdrop of Upper Wharfedale & Littondale, nestles in the Yorkshire Dales with the climbers' challenge, Kilnsey Crag, on the doorstep. The area is famous for walking & cycling with many footpaths, including the Dales Way, close by. At nearby Kilnsey you can book day fishing & food at The Kilnsey Park, or bar snacks at The Tennant Arms Hotel. Pony & Llama trekking & many other activities are also nearby. The barn provides warm, comfortable accommodation for walking, cycling, friends or family groups.

 GROUPS ONLY

DETAILS
- **Open** - All year.
- **Beds** - 20: 2x2 (twin), 2x4, 1x8.
- **Price/night** - From £16 per person.

CONTACT:
Tel: 01756 636350
info@skirfarebarn.com
www.skirfarebarn.com
Kettlewell Rd, Kilnsey, North Yorkshire, BD23 5PT

KETTLEWELL
HOSTEL
65b

The multi award winning Kettlewell Hostel is a stylish Independent Youth Hostel in the heart of the Yorkshire Dales. Serving hearty, great value homemade meals & local beer in the large dining room. There's a cosy lounge with woodburner, a lovely garden, self-catering kitchen & big bike shed! Sleeps up to 42 in 11 bedrooms. Great walking and cycling routes on the doorstep

DETAILS
- **Open** - All year. Reception 8-10am, 4-9pm.
- **Beds** - 42: 1 x twin, 1 x double, 4x3, 2x4, 2x6, 1x5/6
- **Price/night** - Beds from £27.50, private rooms for 2 from £65. Sole use from £650. YHA discount on our website.

CONTACT: Saul & Floss Ward
Tel: 01756 760232
hello@thekettlewellhostel.co.uk
www.thekettlewellhostel.co.uk
Whernside House, Kettlewell, Skipton, North Yorkshire, BD23 5QU

WHARFESIDE
HOUSE
66a

In the village of Kettlewell in the Yorkshire Dales National Park, Wharfeside house provides self-catering accommodation for sole use groups of 15-30 people. Facilities include a well equipped, fully fitted kitchen with Aga cooker and fridge freezer, shower facilities with separate male and female toilets, a large communal space, drying area and large indoor bike/equipment store. Onsite parking for 4 vehicles.

        GROUPS ONLY

DETAILS
■ **Open** - All year round including Christmas and New Year, 24 hours.
■ **Beds** - 30: 2x8, 1x6, 1x4, 2x2
■ **Price/night** - £350 per night - plus £5 per person for hygiene and linen. All bookings get sole use. Midweek offers.

CONTACT: John Yorke
Tel: 07906 871801
bookings@wharfeside.org
wharfeside.org
Middle Lane, Kettlewell, Skipton
BD23 5QX

INGLETON YHA
GRETA TOWER
66b

On the edge of the Yorkshire Dales, surrounded by magnificent countryside with caves, waterfalls and mountains, Ingleton is dominated by Ingleborough, the best known of Yorkshire's Three Peaks (this is a great base for The Challenge). Known for its walking routes and waterfall trail, the area has plenty for walkers, climbers, mountain bikers and cavers. Licensed and serving tasty meals there is also a self-catering kitchen. Perfect for families and school trips.

DETAILS
■ **Open** - All year. (Sole use only Nov - Feb). Reception 8am-10am & 5-10pm
■ **Beds** - 64: 4x6, 2x5, 7x4, 1x2,
■ **Price/night** - Beds from £25, rooms from £59. Sole use bookings welcome.

CONTACT: Manager
Tel: 015242 41444
ingleton@yha.org.uk
www.ingletonhostel.co.uk
Greta Tower, Sammy Lane, Ingleton,
North Yorkshire, LA6 3EG

DALES LODGE

67a

THE OLD SCHOOL
BUNKHOUSE

67b

Dales Lodge offers luxury hostel style accommodation on the outskirts of Ingleton in the Yorkshire Dales. Oozing quality with a Swiss chalet feel, the Lodge sleeps 28 across 6 rooms. With underfloor heating throughout. A small meeting room with climbing wall, whiteboard and TV is available to hire and outdoor activities can be organised.

Book a bed, a room or the whole place. It's perfect for a family holiday, a weekend away or a gathering of friends.

Situated near Ingleton in the Yorkshire Dales, on the Yorkshire Three Peaks route, The Old School Bunkhouse sleeps up to 26. It has a comfortable lounge, with TV, DVD & WiFi, a large kitchen diner, 4 bathrooms & a drying room with washing machine. Outside is parking for 12 cars and great views of Ingleborough and Whernside. The pub over the road is ideal for that celebratory drink

DETAILS

- **Open** - All year.   Check in 4-8pm. Check out by 10am or by arrangement.
- **Beds** - 28: 2x8, 2x4, 2x double ensuite
- **Price/night** - Dorm: £35.   £145 dbl; £150 4 bed; £175 8 bed; sole use £650

DETAILS

- **Open** - All year.
- **Beds** - Sleeps 26: 2x6, 2x5, 2x2
- **Price/night** - Midweek £350. Weekend £450. Bank Holiday Weekends (3-night minimum booking) £500 per night.   Plus £5pp per stay for duvet hire if required.

CONTACT: Sam Perkins
Tel: 01524 805724
daleslodge@gmail.com
daleslodge.co.uk
Kirkstead, Tatterthorn Ln, Ingleton, Carnforth, North Yorkshire LA6 3DU

CONTACT: Debbie Bryant
Tel: 07909 223819
bookings@oldschoolbunkhouse.co.uk
www.oldschoolbunkhouse.co.uk
Hawes Road, Chapel le Dale, Ingleton, LA6 3AR

BROADRAKE
BUNKBARN
68a

HAWKS
BARN
68b

Broadrake Bunkbarn offers direct access to the Three Peaks Challenge Walk which can be started from the door. It is an ideal stopover on the Pennine Journey or Dales High Way. This popular accommodation for 20 has an upstairs open-plan living space with excellent self-catering & communal facilities. Perfect for extended family reunions, cyclists, cavers and dark sky enthusiasts. Individuals, couples and small groups welcome mid-week.

Luxury accommodation for 6 + 3 kids in the centre of the Yorkshire Three Peaks. Hawks Barn sits in a sleepy hamlet just a 10 min walk from Horton-in-Ribblesdale. With easy access to the Pennine Way, the Pennine Bridleway, the 3 Peaks Challenge and other routes it makes a fantastic base for an adventure in the Yorkshire Dales National Park. Run on the lines of a ski chalet you can opt for catered meals or self-cater.

DETAILS

- **Open** - All year. All day.
- **Beds** - 20: 1x8, 2x4, 2x twin.
- **Price/night** - Weekends: £975 for 2 nights sole use. Mid-week: £25pp or £395 a night sole use. £7pp bedding/towel hire.

CONTACT: Mike & Rachel Benson
Tel: 01524 241357
info@broadrake.co.uk
www.broadrake.co.uk
Broadrake, Chapel-le-Dale, Ingleton, LA6 3AX

DETAILS

- **Open** - All year.
- **Beds** - 6/9: 3x2 (twin or superking) + 3 under-bed singles.
- **Price/night** - From £38pp. Min cost £175pn. Min stay 2 nights.

CONTACT: Tilly or Wayne
Tel: 07709 800351 or 01729 878115
hello@yorkshirestays.co.uk
www.yorkshirestays.co.uk/tour-hawks-barn
The Old Shippon, Horton-in-Ribblesdale, Settle, North Yorkshire. BD24 0JE

CHAPEL GALLERY
BUNKHOUSE
69a

Situated in the market town of Hawes in Wensleydale, Chapel Gallery Bunkhouse offers comfortable accommodation for up to 10 guests. Book a bed in a dorm, a private room (sleeps 5) or the whole bunkhouse.

With The Pennine Way on the doorstep, and easy access to footpaths, bridleways as well as the famous Yorkshire 3 Peaks, the bunkhouse is perfect for walkers, cyclists and runners.

DETAILS
- **Open** - All year.
- **Beds** - 10: 2x5 (bunks + 1 single bed)
- **Price/night** - Bed £30. Room (sleeps 5) £150. Whole Bunkhouse £300. (Generally sole use Fri & Sat).

CONTACT: Ellie & John
Tel: 07474 138536 or 01969 667584
info@chapelgalleryhawes.com
chapelgalleryhawes.com
Burtersett Road, Hawes, North Yorks, DL8 3NP

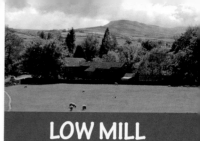

LOW MILL
OUTDOOR CENTRE
69b

Low Mill Outdoor Centre, a not-for-profit charity, lies on the edge of the pretty village of Askrigg in Wensleydale in the Yorkshire Dales.

With good access to many walks, cycle routes, rivers, climbs and caves it is the perfect base for all types of groups; schools, clubs and friend & family get-togethers.

      **GROUPS ONLY**

DETAILS
- **Open** - All year
- **Beds** - 40: Main Building: 26: 1x14, 1x6, 1x4, 1x2. The Wing: 14: 1x8, 1x4, 1x2.
- **Price/night** - Whole Centre bookings only: W/E: 2 nights £2,500. Mid wk: 3 nights £3,000, 4 nights £3,500

CONTACT: Low Mill
Tel: 01969 650432
info@lowmill.com
www.lowmill.com
Station Road, Askrigg, Leyburn, North Yorkshire DL8 3HZ

KIRKBY STEPHEN
HOSTEL
70a

NEW ING
LODGE
70b

Former Methodist Church with a range of accommodation for individuals, families and groups amongst beautiful authentic features; stained glass, arches and panels. There's a large dining room & kitchen and a quiet lounge in the gallery. Kirkby Stephen is a market town in the upper Eden Valley. On Wainwright's Coast to Coast path with easy access to the Pennine Journey, the W2W cycle route, the Howgill Hills, the Yorkshire Dales and the Lake District.

11-bedroom farmhouse offering comfortable & friendly B&B, dormitory & camping accommodation on the eastern edge of the Lake District. Also available for exclusive use hire. Shap is in the Eden Valley, just off the M6, on the edge of the Lake District National Park. The Howgills & the Pennine Fells are close by. On Wainwright's Coast to Coast, the Westmorland Way & the Miller's Way. It's perfect for large groups or individuals.

DETAILS

- **Open** - All year. Please arrive after 5pm (or ring to arrange arrival).
- **Beds** - 38: 1x8, 3x6, 2x4, 1x2, 1x3 ensuite
- **Price/night** - £26.50pp

DETAILS

- **Open** - All year.
- **Beds** - 21: 4x dbl rooms, 2x family (dbl + 2 singles), 2x triple, 2x 4-bedded dorms.
- **Price/night** - Dorm £30pp. B&B (private rooms) from £75pp. Exclusive use from £900pn.

CONTACT: Denise
Tel: 07812 558525
kirkbystephenhostel@btconnect.com
www.kirkbystephenhostel.co.uk
Market Street, Kirkby Stephen, Cumbria, CA17 4QQ

CONTACT: Eva
Tel: 01931 716719 or 07792 222881
info@newinglodge.co.uk
www.newinglodge.co.uk
New Ing Lodge, Main Street, Shap, Penrith, Cumbria, CA10 3LX

REAGILL
VILLAGE HALL
71a

GREENGILL
BARN
71b

Reagill Village Hall offers simple budget accommodation to C2C walkers, cyclists, families & outdoor enthusiasts. Situated in a tiny hamlet of just 20 houses, there are no street lights, little traffic and wonderful dark skies for star gazing. There are plenty of lovely walks from the doorstep, while Shap is 3 miles away, Appleby 10 miles and Penrith 12 miles. Facilities include a kitchen with a new cooker, fridge & microwave, 2 new multi stove heaters and a new power shower. Blow up mattresses are provided (1 dbl, 2 twin, 2 kid's). BYO bedding.

DETAILS

■ **Open** - All year. Closed Mondays during term time.
■ **Beds** - 6+: 1xdbl, 2xtwin, 2xchilds (all blow up beds) + floor space
■ **Price/night** - £12pp. Min charge £25.

CONTACT: Margaret Wilcox
Tel: 01931 715320 or 07804 291972
margaret.wilcox@talk21.com
Fern Bank, Reagill, Cumbria. CA10 3ER

A converted traditional barn on the edge of Morland in Cumbria's rolling Eden Valley. Close to the Lake District and handy for the M6. Great for gatherings of family or friends wanting to visit the Lake District, the Pennines, the Yorkshire Dales and the Borders. There is a large, fully equipped kitchen/dining room and a large, two-storey games room. On NCR 71 and Wiggo's Loop on C2C. Good local walking and easy access to lakes & fells. Local café and pub for meals & ale.

DETAILS

■ **Open** - Open from April to December.
■ **Beds** - 16: 2x8
■ **Price/night** - Min 3 nights: £800 for first 3 nights then £160 per subsequent night. 7th night free. BYO own bedding.

CONTACT: Sabine Wood
Tel: 01931 234543
greengillholidays@gmail.com
www.greengillholidays.co.uk
Greengill Barn, Strickland Road, Morland, Penrith, Cumbria CA10 3AX

YEALAND
OLD SCHOOL
72a

WITHERSLACK
CYCLE BARN
72b

Yealand Old School provides newly refurbished, self-catering accommodation with en suite bedrooms and group dorms. Relax in the grounds of the Quaker Meeting House. A short stroll from Summerhouse Hill and Warton Crag amidst spectacular limestone scenery and nature reserves. LEJOG passes the front door on Route 6. Quiet village location, pub currently closed.

Between Grange Over Sands and Kendal on the northern shore of Morecambe Bay, within the beautiful Whitbarrow Nature Reserve in the southern Lake District. Built for cyclists and walkers with drying room, laundry, kitchen, diner, lounges, cycle storage, workshop and bike wash. Perfect for groups, families and individuals. Just 500m from the Morecambe Bay Cycle Way, the Lakes & Dales Loop and NCN 700 & 70. E-bike hire is available on site.

DETAILS

- **Open** - All year. Check in between 5-8pm (or by arrangement) Depart by 11am
- **Beds** - 22: 1x2, 2x4, 10x stacking beds, plus mats
- **Price/night** - From £20pp, £10 children 5+. Sole use from £230.

DETAILS

- **Open** - All year. All day
- **Beds** - 14: 2x2(twin) 1x4(family), 1x6.
- **Price/night** - From £27 including bedding and towel. Please call for exclusive use deals and to book meals.

CONTACT: Warden
Tel: 07548 146479
yealandwarden@lancsquakers.org.uk
www.yealandoldschool.co.uk
18 Yealand Rd, Yealand Conyers,
Carnforth, Lancashire LA5 9SH

CONTACT: Steph Fry
Tel: 01539 552223 or 07876 576874
info@beckhead.co.uk
www.witherslackcyclebarn.co.uk
Beck Head Farm, Witherslack, Grange
Over Sands. Cumbria, LA11 6SH

LOWICK SCHOOL
BUNKHOUSE
73a

Within the old primary school at Lowick Green, nestled between Coniston water (4 miles) and Ulverston, the bunkhouse has a lounge with wood-burning stove, large kitchen/dining room opening onto a patio with great views of the mountains and an outdoor area with campfire.

All groups staying in the bunkhouse need to be doing an organised activity.

DETAILS
- **Open** - All year.
- **Beds** - 24: 2x8, 1x4 (one 8 bed can be expanded to 10) + 2 bed annexe option.
- **Price/night** - Sole use from £439 per night at weekends and £275 per night Mon-Thurs. £250 damage deposit. Individual rooms available for mid-week nights and within 4 weeks.

CONTACT: Emma Hoving
Tel: 01539 528666
info@riverdeepmountainhigh.co.uk
riverdeepmountainhigh.co.uk
Lowick Green, Ulverston, LA12 8EB

ROOKHOW
73b

Escape to the heart of the Lake District, leaving the crowds behind. Rookhow is a secluded haven of tranquility, with 12 acres of private ancient woodland nestled between Coniston and Lake Windermere. Stay in the cosy self-catering barn with its log fires and snug sitting room and make use of the campfire, outdoor seating area and yurt in the woods. Hire the historic Quaker Meeting House for extra group space.

DETAILS
- **Open** - All year.
- **Beds** - Beds. 16: 1x2, 1x6, 1x8, plus space for 4 in the yurt and space to camp.
- **Price/night** - Bunkbarn £350 (min 2 nights). Yurt £45, Quaker Meeting House £65. Sole use of whole site £460.

CONTACT: Sue Nicholls
Tel: 07377 971783
contactrookhow@gmail.com
rookhow.org.uk
Rookhow, Rusland, nr Grizedale,
Ulverston, South Lakeland, LA12 8LA

HIGH WALLABARROW
CAMPING BARN
74a

LAKES
HOSTEL
74b

High Wallabarrow is a traditional hill farm in the Duddon Valley, the Lake District's quiet corner. The well equipped camping barn, an old farmhouse, sleeps 10 upstairs. Downstairs there's a large living area with woodburning stove and fully equipped kitchen. Mattresses provided BYO sleeping bags/pillows. Toilet just outside and shower nearby. 15 mins' walk to pub, 10 mins to climbing crag. Not suitable for rowdy groups.

Lakes Hostel is your perfect base for the Lake District. Central village location. No need for taxis or cars to get around. Unique property, 5 colourful, cosy and clean bedrooms (5 star mattresses & bedding) that can cater for individuals, groups, couples and families. Fully fitted kitchen, open plan lounge social space, free super fast WiFi, large TV and workspace for laptops. Windermere village close to all the cafes, restaurants, bus/trains, boat trips, pubs & shops.

DETAILS

- **Open** - All year. Arrive after 4pm, (earlier by arrangement) vacate by 11am.
- **Beds** - 10: 1x10 with extra possible.
- **Price/night** - £12.50pp weeknights in school term. Two-night weekends sole-use £125/night. £1.50 per dog per night.

CONTACT: Chris Chinn (9am to 9pm)
Tel: 01229 715011
camden.chinn@gmail.com
www.wallabarrow.co.uk
High Wallabarrow, Ulpha, Broughton-in-Furness, Cumbria, LA20 6EA

DETAILS

- **Open** - All year. 24 hours with key code
- **Beds** - 19: 1x5 (1 dbl, 1 sgl, 1 bunk), 2x4 (bunks), 2x3 (1 dbl, 1 sgl)
- **Price/night** - From £55pp Sun-Thurs, £60 pp Fri-Sat. Min 2 nights. See website.

CONTACT: Amanda
Tel: 07977 414697
info@lakeshostel.co.uk
lakeshostel.co.uk
1, High Street, Windermere, Cumbria, LA23 1AF

MAGGS HOWE
CAMPING BARN

75a

DACRES STABLE
CAMPING BARN

75b

You'll find Maggs Howe Camping Barn In the quiet, unspoilt valley of Kentmere. It's a ramblers' paradise with woods, fields, lanes, a scattering of traditional farms & the fells covered with Wainwright walks.

There is plenty to do including biking, riding & fishing, as well as quiet enjoyment. Maggs Howe provides B&B in 3 farmhouse rooms and a camping barn (BYO sleeping bag). Breakfast (£8) and suppers (from £14) are available with notice. Dogs need prior permission.

A short drive from Kendal, Dacres Stable Camping Barn is on the eastern edge of the Lake District National Park. On a gated road away from the main A6 it is a perfect base for exploring the Yorkshire Dales, the Lake District and the Eden Valley. Great too for mountain biking, walking, & cycling on quiet tracks and lanes. The camping barn sleeps up to 8 on a sole use, self-catering basis.

DETAILS

■ **Open** - Easter to November
■ **Beds** - 8
■ **Price/night** - Sole use of the building. Ground floor only (sleeps 2+) £55. Ground floor plus upper bunk room £85. Minimum 2 nights stay. Reductions for longer stays.

DETAILS

■ **Open** - All year. 24 hours.
■ **Beds** - Camping Barn 10: 1x6, 1x4. B&B 8: 1x4(family), 1x2 (double), 1x2 (twin).
■ **Price/night** - Barn: £15pp. B&B: £32-£35pp.

CONTACT: Christine Hevey
Tel: 01539 821689
c.hevey@btinternet.com
Kentmere, Kendal, Cumbria, LA8 9JP

CONTACT: Hilary Fell
Tel: 01539 823208 or 07788 633936
hilaryfell@btinternet.com
dacresstablecampingbarn.blogspot.com
Grisedale Farm, Whinfell, Kendal, Cumbria, LA8 9EN

RYDAL HALL
BUNKHOUSE
76a

THE OLD CAFE
BUNKROOM
76b

Rydal Hall Bunkhouse provides group accommodation for up to 25 in four dormitories at the heart of the Lake District. There's a large common room, drying room & a fully equipped stainless steel kitchen. En-suite rooms for up to 50 people are available in The Hall and there is a quiet campsite and eco-pods for individuals/families in the grounds. Dogs welcome by arrangement.

A bijou 2 person bunkroom in the majestic setting of Rydal Country House B&B in the heart of the Lake District. Beautifully appointed, there's a small kitchenette with microwave, toaster, fridge & kettle, one set of bunks, a dining table & a small en suite shower room. Linen & towels are provided, but beds are not made up. Guests are invited to use the bar & lounges in the main house & enjoy the extensive riverside grounds. Superb walking & spectacular mountain scenery. Dogs welcome.

DETAILS

- **Open** - Opening February 2023. All year (excluding xmas). All day.
- **Beds** - Bunkhouse 25: 1x10, 1x9, 1x6, 1x4. Plus campsite, eco-pods & accommodation for 50 in the main hall.
- **Price/night** - Bunkhouse: Sole use £435 (min 2 nights at w/e), Pods: from £45 (min 2 nights at w/e) Dogs: £5pn.

CONTACT: Bookings Office
Tel: 01539 432050
mail@rydalhall.org
www.rydalhall.org
Ambleside, Cumbria, LA22 9LX

DETAILS

- **Open** - All year
- **Beds** - 2 + B&B in the main house
- **Price/night** - From £50 sole use. Dogs £8 per stay (max 2).

CONTACT: Helena & Mark Tendall
Tel: 015394 33208
info@rydallodge.co.uk
www.theoldcafebunkroom.co.uk
Rydal Lodge Country House B&B, Rydal, Ambleside, Cumbria LA22 9LR

ELTERWATER
HOSTEL
77a

GREAT LANGDALE
BUNKHOUSE
77b

Located in the peaceful village of Elterwater, in the Langdale valley, 15 mins' drive from Ambleside. The area has many walks for people of all abilities, from gentle riverside meanders to the challenge presented by the Langdale Pikes, Bowfell and Scafell. Pubs, shops and other amenities are nearby. The area is popular for both on and off-road cycling, rock climbing and other outdoor activities. An ideal overnight stop on the Cumbria Way.

Great Langdale Bunkhouse is situated at the foot of the Langdale fells, amidst some of the finest mountain scenery in England. There's direct access to mountain biking, road cycling, walking, fell running, wild swimming & climbing.

The bunkhouse sleeps 18 across 5 simple but comfortable rooms. Each room has a kettle, double plug socket & free Wifi. The bunkhouse has biomass central heating throughout so it's toasty warm with an endless supply of hot water & powerful showers. Secure bike storage available on request.

DETAILS

- **Open** - All year (Nov-Feb groups only). Access 7.30am-11.30pm. Reception 7.30-10am & 5-10pm.
- **Beds** - 38 : 6x2, 1x4, 1x4 ensuite, 3x6
- **Price/night** - From £25pp. Check website for special offers.Call for sole use.

CONTACT: Nick Owen
Tel: 01539 437245
bookings@elterwaterhostel.co.uk
www.elterwaterhostel.co.uk
Elterwater, Ambleside LA22 9HX

DETAILS

- **Open** - All year. All day.
- **Beds** - 18: 2x6, 3x2
- **Price/night** - From £21.50 per person.

CONTACT: Vicky
Tel: 07886 421313 or 07305 526413
vixkaye@gmail.com
www.greatlangdalebunkhouse.co.uk
Great Langdale Bunkhouse, Great Langdale, Ambleside, LA22 9JU

ALMOND LODGE
HELVELLYN
78a

78b
SHEPHERDS
CROOK

Almond Lodge is a newly refurbished luxury group hostel perched 1/3 of the way up Helvellyn in the Lake District. Sleeping up to 28 across 4 rooms with breathtaking views from every window, the Lodge is perfect for groups of walkers, climbers, cyclists, runners, swimmers or friends and families in need of some mountain therapy. The village of Glenridding with local shops, nice pubs and restaurants and the southern end of Ullswater is just over 1 mile away.

Noran Bank Farm is near Ullswater just through Patterdale in Cumbria, just 5 minutes' walk away from the Coast to Coast route and The Westmorland Way.

Shepherd's Crook Bunkhouse is a barn converted to a very high standard and sleeps 8. Duvets, linen and towels are provided. DIY breakfast and packed lunches can be pre-booked. It is very popular with Coast to Coasters, walkers, cyclists and for family/friends get-togethers.

DETAILS
- **Open** - All year
- **Beds** - 28: 3x8, 1x4
- **Price/night** - Sole use from £350 mid week, £420 on weekend nights. Plus £60 per stay service charge.

DETAILS
- **Open** - All year.
- **Beds** - 8: 1x6, 1x2 + B&B.
- **Price/night** - £25pp. Sole use £150. Farmhouse B&B £36pp.

CONTACT: Jon
Tel: 0 779944 0557
jon@almondlodgehelvellyn.com
almondlodgehelvellyn.com
Almond Lodge Helvellyn, Greenside
Road, Glenridding. CA11 0QR

CONTACT: Mrs Heather Jackson
Tel: 01768 482327 or 07833 981504
heathernoranbank@gmail.com
www.noranbank.co.uk
Noran Bank Farm, Patterdale, Penrith,
Cumbria, CA11 0NR

ST JOHNS IN THE VALE
CAMPING BARN
79a

St John's-in-the-Vale Camping Barn is an 18th century stable on a peaceful hill farm, with stunning views to Blencathra, Helvellyn and Castle Rock. The Barn has a sleeping area upstairs (mattresses provided) and a kitchen and sitting/dining area below. A separate toilet and shower are within the building. A wood-burning stove makes it nice and cosy. Outside there is a BBQ area. The star-filled night skies are magical. Self catering cottage also available (sleeping 4).

DETAILS
- **Open** - All year. All day.
- **Beds** - Barn 8: 1x8
- **Price/night** - Barn: From £15pp. Minimum £40 a night. £120 Friday and Saturday. Minimum 2 night stays.

CONTACT: Sarah
Tel: 017687 79242
info@campingbarn.com
www.campingbarn.com
Low Bridge End Farm, St John's-in-the-Vale, Keswick, CA12 4TS

THE WHITE HORSE
INN BUNKHOUSE
79b

The White Horse Inn has 2 bunkhouses in the converted stables of this traditional Lake District inn at the foot of Blencathra

Guests are welcome in the Inn which has great pub food, open fires, local ales and is open from 11am to 11pm. Each bunkhouse has a basic kitchen, dining area and bunkrooms sleeping between 4 and 6. Paths to the mountains from the garden & the C2C route passes the door.

DETAILS
- **Open** - All year. All day access.
- **Beds** - 48: Bunkhouse 26: 1x6, 5x4. Bunkhouse 22: 3x6, 1x4
- **Price/night** - £16pp. 4 bed room £64. 6 bed room £96. Bedding £5/stay. Enquire for Xmas/New Year.

CONTACT: Phil or Cozmin
Tel: 017687 79883
info@thewhitehorse-blencathra.co.uk
www.thewhitehorse-blencathra.co.uk
The White Horse Inn, Scales, Nr Threlkeld, Keswick, CA12 4SY

LOWSIDE FARM
CAMPING BARN & PODS
80a

Nestling at the foot of Blencathra, with paths to the mountains from the doorstep Lowside Farm Camping Barn & Pods are your perfect Lake District base.

Sleeping groups of up to 14, the newly converted camping barn is modern & comfortable, The six, 4 berth luxury camping pods, provide extra accommodation for larger groups, older family members and those with small chilldren. All bedding is provided.

       GROUPS ONLY

DETAILS
- **Open** - All year
- **Beds** - 38: Bunkhouse 14: 1x12,1x2. Pods 24: 6x4
- **Price/night** - £30pp. Min 8 people. Min 2 nights. Enquire for pods.

CONTACT:
Tel: 07887 645229
microlodges@btinternet.com
lowsidefarm.co.uk/camping-barn/
Lowside Farm, Troutbeck, Penrith, Cumbria CA11 0SX

BLAKEBECK FARM
CAMPING BARN
80b

At the foot of Souther Fell, within easy reach of Blencathra, Blakebeck Farm is set amidst the wildflower meadows of Mungrisdale. On the C2C cycle route & the Cumbrian Way. Perfect as a weekend break for walkers. The large upstairs room has bunk beds for 8 people (BYO sleeping bags) & a large farmhouse table. The kitchen has all you need to cook a simple meal and cooked breakfasts are available on request. One dog by prior arrangement. Not suitable for parties. No children under 11 years.

DETAILS
- **Open** - All year. All day
- **Beds** - 8: 1x8 + holiday cottages
- **Price/night** - £15pp. No children under 11.

CONTACT: Judith
Tel: 017687 79957 or 07789 287121
j.egan001@btinternet.com
blakebeckfarm.co.uk
Blakebeck, Mungrisdale, Penrith, CA11 0SZ

BASSENTHWAITE
PARISH ROOM
81a

Refurbished to a very high standard, the Parish Room is a great base for outdoors enthusiasts to explore Skiddaw, the Northern Lakes, Keswick and the Cumbrian coast.

There is a modern well-equipped kitchen, large hall, meeting room with sofa and large TV. There is also disabled access throughout. Separate male/female toilets and two shower rooms. Bring your own beds, bedding and towels. Free WiFi. Sorry no stag/hen parties.

DETAILS

- **Open** - All year
- **Beds** - 18 (BYO beds/bedding/towels)
- **Price/night** - £180 for 18 people (larger and smaller groups please get in touch for price). Two night minimum stay.

CONTACT: Louise
bookbassenthwaiteparishroom@gmail.com
www.bassenthwaite.org.uk
School Road, Bassenthwaite, Keswick, CA12 4QJ

CALDBECK
GLAMPING BARNS
81b

Caldbeck Glamping accommodation is in the centre of Caldbeck village close to Wainwright's Northern Fells. Opposite The Odd Fellows pub and close to the village store. The self contained barns sleep 8 and 6. Three people can sleep in the Bothy and there is space for a small tent or two. Caldbeck is a 25 minute drive from M6 and right on The Cumbria Way and The Reivers Cycle route. Sit back and enjoy everything this hidden Lake District village has to offer.

DETAILS

- **Open** - All year
- **Beds** - 17: Hayloft 8:1x8, High Pike 6:1x6, The Bothy 3:1x3 plus 4 camping
- **Price/night** - From: Hayloft £225. High Pike £170. Bothy £130. All barns: £525

CONTACT: John Nicoll
Tel: 0741 0694305
johnnicoll10@gmail.com
www.caldbeckglamping.com
Caldbeck, Lake District, Cumbria, CA7 8EA

SKIDDAW HOUSE
HOSTEL
82a

82b
DENTON
HOUSE

The highest hostel in Britain! Escape the crowds at this remote mountain hostel. Hire the whole place for a small group of friends or family. No roads, no other buildings, no phone signal: just uninterrupted beautiful mountain views. An easy walk or mountain bike ride from Keswick or Threlkeld. Rustic but comfortable with a wood burning stove, hot showers, a well-stocked shop/bar and full bedding provided.

Denton House is a purpose built hostel in the lake District offering bunkhouse accommodation.

Warm and well equipped for self-catering, the centre was designed for groups with parking for 40 cars.

There is equipment storage and access to the River Greta across the road.

DETAILS	DETAILS

■ **Open** - Open from April 2023. Check in from 5pm; please contact the hostel if you would prefer to arrive a little earlier.
■ **Beds** - 20 : 1x8, 2x5, 1x2
■ **Price/night** - Enquire for individuals. Sole use from £500 per night. Minimum of 2 nights for winter bookings.

■ **Open** - All year (including Christmas). Office hours 9am - 5pm.
■ **Beds** - 66: 1x14, 2x10, 1x8, 2x6, 3x4
■ **Price/night** - £22 midweek, £25 weekend. Sole use £999 (midweek). Breakfast £6. Pack lunch £6. Dinner £10.

CONTACT: Sue Edwards
skiddaw@yha.org.uk
www.skiddawhouse.co.uk
Bassenthwaite, Keswick, Cumbria,
CA12 4QX

CONTACT: Christina
Tel: 01768 775351
keswickhostel@hotmail.co.uk
www.dentonhouse-keswick.co.uk
Penrith Road, Keswick, Cumbria,
CA12 4JW

DERWENTWATER
INDEPENDENT HOSTEL
83a

Derwentwater Independent Hostel is a stunning Georgian mansion, standing in its own spacious grounds between the Falls & the Lake, with stunning mountain views. Just 2 miles from Keswick, close to the Coast to Coast route and the delights of Borrowdale, it makes a great base for individuals, families, and groups of all types. Book a bed, a room, a camping pod or take over the hostel.

DETAILS
- **Open** - All year. 7am - 11pm.
- **Beds** - 84: 1x2, 3x4, 4x6, 3x8, 1x22 + 3 Camping Pods
- **Price/night** - From £25 (adult), £24 (child). Family rooms from £72. Camping pods from £50. Camping from £10pp per night.

CONTACT:
Tel: 01768 777246
reception@derwentwater.org
www.derwentwater.org
Barrow House, Borrowdale, Keswick, Cumbria, CA12 5UR

HAWSE END
CENTRE
83b

Hawse End Centre in the Lake District sits at the head of the magnificent Borrowdale Valley on the shores of Derwentwater. Guests enjoy easy access to Keswick and the mountains beyond via launch or lakeside walk.

The house is a large, comfortable, country mansion ideal for large groups, while the Cottage is more suited to smaller groups or large families.

Outdoor activities can be arranged.

DETAILS
- **Open** - All year.
- **Beds** - 73: House 49: (10 rooms). Cottage 24: (7 rooms) + camping
- **Price/night** - Enquire for prices.

CONTACT:
Tel: 01768 812280
cumbriaoutdoors.enquiries@cumbria.gov.uk
cumbriaoutdoors.org
Portinscale, Keswick, Cumbria, CA12 5UE

BOWDERSTONE
BUNKHOUSE
84a

HIGH HOUSE
84b

Bowderstone Bunkhouse is situated along the Borrowdale Valley by the famous Bowderstone – a massive boulder that has lain precariously on one side for the last 10,000 years! It has a kitchen, accessible shower room and communal area, plus running water, electricity and drainage, but linen and mattresses not provided. Please note, Bowderstone Bunkhouse is only for use by clubs, educational groups or other organisations such as the Scouts, as it is on National Trust land and has certain restrictions to its use.

High House in Seathwaite, at the head of the beautiful valley of Borrowdale, offers comfortable bunkhouse accommodation. Popular with walking/climbing clubs and educational groups, early booking is advised. Group bookings only. Large common room with stove (coke/coal). Fully equipped self catering kitchen, 2 washrooms/toilets and a shower. Drying room. Large grounds with tables, benches and firepit. Accessible by car. Club members may occasionally use a 3rd dorm unless exclusive use is booked (midweek only).

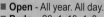

DETAILS
- **Open** - All year.
- **Beds** - 12
- **Price/night** - £100 per night

CONTACT: Reception at the Lake District
Calvert Trust
Tel: 017687 72255
enquiries@calvertlakes.org.uk
www.calvertlakes.org.ukGrange,
Keswick, CA12 5XA

DETAILS
- **Open** - All year. All day.
- **Beds** - 26: 1x18, 1x8
- **Price/night** - £190 + £25 exclusive use supplement if required (midweek only).

CONTACT: Maja While
bookings.kff@gmail.com
highhouseborrowdale.co.uk
Seathwaite, Borrowdale, Keswick
CA12 5XJ

LOW GILLERTHWAITE
FIELD CENTRE
85a

In the Ennerdale Valley, one of the most beautiful, least spoilt and quietest in the Lake District, Low GIllerthwaite Field Centre sits at the foot of Pillar and Red Pike. Well equipped for groups it is the perfect base for fell walking, rock climbing, bird & wildlife watching, mountain biking, orienteering & canoeing. The centre generates its own hydro-electricity. Vehicle access is by forest track and a BT payphone is on site as most mobiles do not work here.

DETAILS
- **Open** - All year (except Christmas and Boxing Day). 24 hours.
- **Beds** - 40: 2x4, 1x8, 1x10, 1x14.
- **Price/night** - From £11.50 per person (children and students), £15.50 (adults). Camping is £5 per person.

CONTACT: Ellen or Walter
Tel: 01946 861229 or 7736803756
Warden@lgfc.org.uk
www.lgfc.org.uk
Ennerdale, Cleator, CA23 3AX

THE WILD WOOL
BARN
85b

Nestled in the peace of the Ennerdale Valley, overlooking Ennerdale Water. The Wild Wool Barn provides luxury bunkhouse accommodation for 6 (plus 6 camping). Traditional wood-burning stove, electric heating, cooker and shower marry tradition with luxury. With no mobile signal or WiFi The Wild Wool Barn is a true chance to get away and explore the rarely visited Western Lakes. Perfect for camping at Ennerdale Bridge

DETAILS
- **Open** - All year.
- **Beds** - 6: 1x6 + 6 camping
- **Price/night** - From 1 night £150 to 7 nights £700 (low season). Exclusive use 6 + 6 camping: from 1 night £215 to 7 nights £1155. Bank hols min 3 nights. Camping £12pp.

CONTACT: Susan Denham-Smith
Tel: 01946 861270
susan@wildwoolworkshop.co.uk
www.wildwoolbarn.co.uk
Routen Cottage, Ennerdale, CA23 3AU

MILL COTTAGE
BUNKHOUSE
86a

HAGGS BANK
BUNKHOUSE & CAMPING
86b

Close to the historic Nenthead mines in the centre of the North Pennines AONB, Mill Cottage sleeps 6 in an upstairs bunkroom. Each bunk has blinds for privacy & an internal light & shelf.

Downstairs is a small well equipped kitchen and a sitting/dining room. Optional continental breakfast (£2pp). Cafe, shop and bike repair in the village close by. On the C2C cycle route and close to Isaac's Tea Trail.

Perfect for cyclists and walkers alike.

Set in the stunning North Pennines AONB, England's last wilderness. This modern conversion of a historic mine building provides warm accommodation with excellent hot showers for lovers of the great outdoors. Isaac's Tea Trail and the C2C pass right by. There are self catering facilities and meals can be provided for groups. The campsite has tiered pitches and views across the Nent valley. Electric hook-ups, secure cycle storage and plenty of parking.

DETAILS

- **Open** - All year. All day access.
- **Beds** - 25: 1x4/5, 1x9, 1x11
- **Price/night** - £20pp. Sole use £400, £1080 (3 nights). Camping: £12, U15, £7. Motorhomes/caravans £25 up to 2.

DETAILS

- **Open** - All year. All day
- **Beds** - 6: 1x6
- **Price/night** - £18pp. Sole use £60. Continental breakfast £2pp.

CONTACT: Sarah Dalzell
Tel: 01434 381023
millcottagebunkhouse@gmail.com
millcottagebunkhouse.com
Nenthead, Alston, Cumbria, CA9 3PD

CONTACT: Danny Taylor
Tel: 07919 092403 or 01434 382486
info@haggsbank.com
haggsbank.com
Haggs Bank Bunkhouse, Nentsbury,
Alston, Cumbria, CA9 3LH

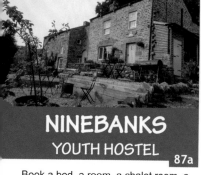

NINEBANKS
YOUTH HOSTEL
87a

Book a bed, a room, a chalet room, a wing or the whole hostel. Ninebanks 4* Hostel, in stunning rural Northumberland, has en-suite bedrooms, a sitting room with log-burner and a spacious dining room. In the chalet are two high quality studio rooms, fully self-contained and separate from the hostel. Dogs welcome with prior notice for sole use or in the chalet. In the North Pennines close to Hadrian's Wall and on Isaac's Tea Trail.

DETAILS
- **Open** - All year. All day. Office 5-10pm.
- **Beds** - 33: Hostel 28: 2x2/3, 2x4, 1x6, 1x8. Chalets: 1xdbl. 1xdbl + single
- **Price/night** - Beds from £24. Rooms from £42. Whole hostel from £250. Chalet from £54. Dogs incur a cleaning fee.

CONTACT: Pauline or Ian
Tel: 01434 345288
contact@ninebanks.org.uk
www.ninebanks.org.uk
Orchard House, Mohope, Hexham,
Northumberland NE47 8DQ

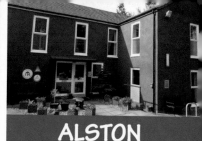

ALSTON
YOUTH HOSTEL
87b

Alston Youth Hostel is within the historic town of Alston nestled in the North Pennines on the eastern side of Cumbria.
Situated directly on the Pennine Way and Isaac's Tea Trail and also about halfway on the very popular Coast to Coast (C2C) cycle route with great indoor cycle storage. The perfect stop-over for walkers and cyclists. You'll receive a warm welcome, Exclusive hire also available!

DETAILS
- **Open** - All year. 8am-10am, 5pm-10pm
- **Beds** - 28 : 2x1, 2x4 (or twin), 3x6
- **Price/night** - Private rooms from £30. Discount of 10% for YHA members. Sole use from £400 for 1 night midweek and from £500 per night Fri-Sat.

CONTACT: Linda or Neil Willmott
Tel: 01434 381509
alston@yha.org.uk
alstonyouthhostel.co.uk/
The Firs, Alston, Cumbria, CA9 3RW

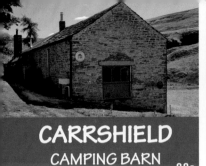

CARRSHIELD
CAMPING BARN
88a

GARRIGILL
VILLAGE HALL
88b

Surrounded by the stunning North Pennines, Carrshield Camping Barn offers basic accommodation for 18 across 3 rooms, each with a wood-burner & a wooden sleeping platform. There's a separate cooking area & a composting WC. BYO stove, utensils & sleeping bag/mat. On the Isaac Tea Trail, C2C cycle route & close to mountain bike routes. Camping may be available.

Perfect for the Pennine Way or C2C cycle route. In the lovely village of Garrigill, the bunkroom above the village hall sleeps 8 with bedding hire available. Larger groups can BYO bedding and use the hall itself where 12 camp beds are available. There is free WiFi, a well equipped kitchen, showers and drying room. It makes the ideal long distance walk/C2C stop over.

DETAILS

■ **Open** - All year. Check in 3pm, check out 10am
■ **Beds** - 18: 1x8, 1x6, 1x4
■ **Price/night** - 8 bed room £60, 6 bed £50, 4 bed £40. Includes a basket of logs. Whole barn £135 (use code THEWHOLEBARNPLEASE).

DETAILS

■ **Open** - All year. All day
■ **Beds** - 35: Bunkroom: 8 bunks. Main Hall: 12 camp beds + floor space for 15.
■ **Price/night** - £18pp. Bunkroom bedding hire (if required) £5 pp per stay. Camping £8 pp (DofE or other youth activity groups half price).

CONTACT: Paul Stafford
Tel: 07896 900956.
carrshieldcampingbarn@gmail.com
www.carrshieldcampingbarn.co.uk
Near Blue Row Cottages, Carrshield, Hexham, NE47 8AF.

CONTACT: Bookings Secretary
Tel: 01434 647516
bookings@garrigillvh.org
www.garrigillvh.org.uk
Garrigill Village Hall, Garrigill, Alston, Cumbria, CA9 3DS

CARRS FARM
BUNKHOUSE
90a

Carrs Farm Bunkhouse is a converted 17th century barn with stunning views over Weardale. It provides comfortable bunk bed accommodation for groups of up to 21 people in three rooms. There is a fully equipped self catering kitchen, games/lounge area and outdoor seating with BBQ.

Situated on a working farm at the heart of the North Pennines. Guided walks and outdoor activities are available for groups and schools.

DETAILS
- **Open** - All year (Arrival time: from 4pm. Departure time: before 10am)
- **Beds** - 21: 2x6, 1x9
- **Price/night** - £25 per person. Enquire about sole use.

CONTACT: Joy Henderson
Tel: 07592 744 649
joy.henderson@carrsfarm.co.uk
carrsfarm.co.uk
Wolsingham, County Durham, DL13 3BQ

EDMUNDBYERS YHA
AT LOW HOUSE HAVEN
90b

Edmunbyers hostel lies in moorland, close to the Northumberland/County Durham boundary, with fine views. It's just two miles from Derwent Reservoir, for sailing & fishing. Ideal for walking holidays, it's also on the C2C cycle route & is close to Hadrian's Wall & Beamish outdoor museum. Cosy & comfortable with optional home cooked evening meals & breakfasts.

DETAILS
- **Open** - All year (camping Apr-Oct). Check in 5-10pm. Check out 8-10am.
- **Beds** - 31: 1x8, 1x6, 2x5, 1x4, 1x3 plus 14 camping pitches (6 with electric)
- **Price/night** - From £25pp (adult). Room for 3: £70, 4: £90, 5: £90. Discounts for YHA members

CONTACT: Debbie Clarke
Tel: 01207 255651
info@lowhousehaven.co.uk
www.lowhousehaven.co.uk
Low House, Edmundbyers, Consett, Durham, DH8 9NL

ALLENDALE
BUNKHOUSE
91a

91b

HILLSIDE FARM
BUNKBARN

Allendale Bunkhouse sits on the Market Square overlooking the hustle and bustle of this small country town, the fells & River East Allen beyond. Book the whole bunkhouse for up to 26 people.
An oasis for walkers, cyclists, horse riders, families, groups of friends and youth & school groups. Allendale is well served with tea rooms, the Forge art gallery & café, a quirky gift shop, a pharmacy, and three wonderful country pubs, all serving food and dog friendly.

A Georgian working farm, right on Hadrian's Wall National Trail & Cycleway near the Solway Coast AONB. Stunning views over the Solway Firth marshes towards Scotland. Bunkbarn or B&B rooms available.

The bunkbarn has cooking facilities & hot showers and is heated with a bio mass boiler. Breakfast or bacon sandwiches available with notice. The barn is available to walkers, cyclists and peaceful family groups.

       GROUPS ONLY

DETAILS
- **Open** - All year. 8am-8pm.
- **Beds** - 26: 2 doubles, 1 single, 4 quads and 1 five person family room.
- **Price/night** - Please contact us for a quote

DETAILS
- **Open** - March to November
- **Beds** - 12
- **Price/night** - £15pp inc shower. £4.50 full English, £2.50 hot sandwiches.

CONTACT: Linda Beck
Tel: 0797 1768993 or 0779 1707097
welcome@the-dale.co.uk
allendalebunkhouse.co.uk
Market Place, Allendale, Hexham,
NE47 9BD

CONTACT: Mrs Sandra Rudd
Tel: 01228 576398
sandrahillsidefarm@gmail.com
www.hadrianswalkbnb.co.uk
Hillside Farm, Boustead Hill, Burgh-by-Sands, Carlisle, Cumbria, CA5 6AA

WAYFARERS
INDEPENDENT HOSTEL
92a

92b

FLORRIE'S
BUNKHOUSE

Close to Penrith town centre and perfect for the C2C cycle route. Excellent value accommodation for visiting Penrith, the Eden Valley & the North Lake District. Bike storage, cleaning, and maintenance facilities on site. Kitchen & dining, en suite rooms with beds made up, lockers, bedside lights & USB points.

Individuals & groups welcome.

Located right on the Hadrian's Wall National Trail this newly converted bunkhouse is aimed at walkers or cyclists. With drying room and cycle storage this is the perfect stop-over on the trail. Open for individuals from April to October, Florrie's provides a comfortable bed, breakfast and evening meals plus the opportunity to socialise with other guests at the bar. From October through the winter season the bunkhouse is open to groups with self-catering.

DETAILS

- **Open** - Jan-Dec. Office 8-11am, 4-9pm.
- **Beds** - 18: 2x2 (twin), 1x6, 2x4
- **Price/night** - From:- £26pp dorm, £60 twin en-suite. £104 4-Bed room en-suite, £156 6-Bed room en-suite, £77 apartment en suite, £404 whole hostel exclusive use. Towel hire: £1.

DETAILS

- **Open** - April to October (self-catering groups in the winter season).
- **Beds** - 16 (17) : 3x4, 1x4 (or 5 if family)
- **Price/night** - B&B from £25pp. Private rooms available.

CONTACT: Zahava or Ben
Tel: 01768 866011
guests@wayfarershostel.com
www.wayfarershostel.com
19 Brunswick Square, Penrith, Cumbria, CA11 7LR

CONTACT: Rebecca & Joss
Tel: 01697 741704
hello@florriesonthewall.co.uk
florriesonthewall.co.uk
Florrie's on the Wall, Kingbank, Walton, Cumbria, CA8 2DH

SLACK HOUSE
FARM
93a

GREENHEAD
HOSTEL
93b

Slack House Farm is an organic dairy farm overlooking Birdoswald Roman Fort on Hadrian's Wall. On the NCN 72 cycle trail and close to Hadrian's Wall National Trail. The bunk-barn is adjacent to the farm's cheese dairy, bordering the dark-skies of Kielder and the Northumberland National Park. It is heated and meals are available. Camping stoves can be used in the cooking cabin (BYO). Provisions available from the adjacent farm-shop

Situated in the village of Greenhead on both the Pennine Way and Hadrian's Wall, the bunkhouse is ideal for walking the Pennine Way Trail or The Wall Path or for exploring the nearby Roman heritage sites. It has a self-catering kitchen big enough for large groups. The flexible accommodation can be booked by the bed, the room or for sole use. Greenhead hostel/ bunkhouse is run by Greenhead Hotel just over the road.

DETAILS

- **Open** - All year
- **Beds** - 16: 3 rooms. (1x3,1x5, 1x8)
- **Price/night** - £15pp BYO sleeping bag, £25pp with bedding and then £15 subsequent nights. Continental breakfast £3, Barn Supper (two courses) £10.

CONTACT: Dianne Horn
Tel: 01697 747351 or 07900 472342
slackhouseorganicfarm@gmail.com
slackhousefarm.co.uk/accommodation
Slack House Farm, Gilsland Brampton, Cumbria, CA8 7DB

DETAILS

- **Open** - Mar to Sept. Enquire for winter.
- **Beds** - 47: Hostel (Sleeps 40) 4x6, 2x8. Flat (Sleeps 7): 2xdbl, 1xtriple .
- **Price/night** - Dorm £18pp. Six bed room £100. Eight bed room £130. Flat with bathroom £150. Whole Hostel £750 .

CONTACT: Greenhead Hotel & Hostel
Tel: 01697 747411
info@greenheadbrampton.co.uk
www.greenheadhostel.co.uk
Greenhead Hotel, Greenhead, Brampton, Cumbria, CA8 7HG

LOUGHVIEWS
BUNKROOM
94a

Tastefully converted from a stone cowshed, Loughviews Bunkroom, offers comfortable & affordable accommodation for up to 4 guests with a kettle and fridge. Book by the bed or sole use. Occupying an idyllic, secluded position, 2.5 miles along a private track. With Hadrians Wall, the Pennine Journey & the Pennine Way close by it is perfect for walkers. For families it's great for exploring Northumberland National Park.

DETAILS
■ **Open** - All year
■ **Beds** - Bunkroom: 4: 1x4. Cottage: 4: 2x2.
■ **Price/night** - Bunkroom: £25pp. Single occupancy £30. Continental breakfast £5. Enquire for cottage.

CONTACT: Hazel Harris
Tel: 07730 367141
bookings@loughviews.com
loughviews.com
Greenlee Farm, Bardon Mill, Hexham, Northumberland, NE47 7AS

GIBBS HILL
FARM HOSTEL
94b

Gibbs Hill Farm Hostel is on a working hill farm near Once Brewed and Hadrian's Wall and close to the Pennine Way. Designed to reduce energy consumption it is centrally heated throughout. Comprising 3 bunkrooms, 2 shower rooms, 2 toilets, a well equipped kitchen, a comfortable communal area and a large deck where you can enjoy the evening sun. Ideal for families who can book a whole room with private facilities. Study groups welcome. Self catering only.

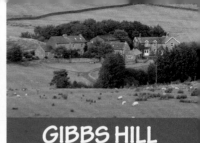

DETAILS
■ **Open** - All year
■ **Beds** - 18: 3x6
■ **Price/night** - £20 adult, £14 child (under 12), minimum of 8 people.

CONTACT: Valerie Gibson
Tel: 01434 344030
val@gibbshillfarm.co.uk
www.gibbshillfarm.co.uk
Gibbs Hill Farm, Bardon Mill, Nr Hexham, Northumberland, NE47 7AP

NEWBROUGH
BUNKHOUSE
95a

In the centre of the village of Newbrough, this community run bunkhouse sleeps 22 across 3 dorms. Facilities include 2 shower/WC rooms, 2 sink areas & a small equipped kitchen. A large communal area is available to groups by arrangement. With footpaths leading directly to Hadrian's Wall, approx 3 miles away, it is popular with walkers. While for cyclists the Sandstone Way & Hadrian's Cycleway pass right by.

DETAILS
■ **Open** - All year. Check in 3pm. Check out before 10am.
■ **Beds** - 22: 2x8, 1x6
■ **Price/night** - £24pp (incl bedding). 6 bed room £90, 8 bed room £118. Whole bunkhouse £292 (bedding £6pp per stay).

CONTACT: Nick Springham
Tel: 07596 081642
info@newbroughbunkhouse.co.uk
www.newbroughbunkhouse.co.uk
The Stanegate, Newbrough, Hexham, Northumberland, NE47 5AR

GREENCARTS
BUNKHOUSES
95b

Greencarts Bunkhouses & Camping are on a working farm in Northumberland National Park. Right next to Hadrian's Wall, they are perfect for walkers or cyclists. There are two accommodation units: The Bunkhouse sleeps 10 in two rooms, while the Barn sleeps 13 in one open plan room. All bedding is provided and continental breakfast is available. There is also a large campsite.

DETAILS
■ **Open** - B/house: 1 Mar-31 Oct. Barn: mid May-31 Aug. All year for large groups.
■ **Beds** - 23: Bunkhouse: 2x5. Barn 1x13
■ **Price/night** - Bunkhouse: £30pp or £40 single occ. Incl. continental b/fast. Barn: £20pp + £5 continental b/fast. Enquire for sole use.

CONTACT: Jean Newton
Tel: 01434 681320
sandra@greencarts.co.uk
greencarts.co.uk
Greencarts Farm, Humshaugh, Northumberland. NE46 4BW

ALLENHEADS
LODGE
89a

BARRINGTON
BUNKHOUSE
89b

Situated in the heart of the North Pennines, Allenheads Lodge is an excellent group venue for outdoor activities or relaxing in the peaceful countryside. An ideal stop on the C2C cycle route it's just 47 miles from the North Sea coast.

Comfortable and well equipped, the lodge has 24 beds in four rooms, central heating, individual toilets and showers and a large kitchen/dining room. The lodge also has drying facilities, bed linen and secure bike storage.

DETAILS
- **Open** - All year. All day.
- **Beds** - 24
- **Price/night** - £250 sole use. Minimum of 3 nights.

CONTACT: Andrea Cowie
Tel: 01915 155300
acowie@springboard-ne.org
Allenheads Lodge, Allenheads,
Northumberland NE47 9HW

Situated in the peaceful village of Rookhope, in Weardale, Barrington Bunkhouse accommodates 15 people. There's room for 13 in the bunkhouse, whilst the adjacent caravan sleeps two.
Camping space is also available.
The kitchen is equipped with two toasters, a kettle, a microwave, electric hob and a fridge. Ideal for cyclists, walkers and family groups. Dogs by arrangement. A warm welcome awaits.

DETAILS
- **Open** - All year. All day.
- **Beds** - 15: Bunkhouse 13. Caravan 2 + camping
- **Price/night** - £24pp incl. snack b/fast. Camping £14 with b/fast, £10 without. Sole use rates negotiable.

CONTACT: Valerie Livingston
Tel: 01388 517656
barrington_bunkhouse@hotmail.co.uk
www.barrington-bunkhouse-rookhope.com
Barrington Cottage, Rookhope,
Weardale, Co. Durham, DL13 2BG

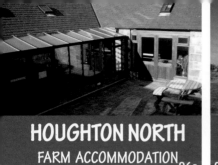

HOUGHTON NORTH
FARM ACCOMMODATION
96a

96b
TARSET TOR
BUNKHOUSE & BOTHIES

Houghton North Farm, partly built with stones from Hadrian's Wall is in the beautiful Northumberland countryside right on the Hadrian's Wall trail, 15 miles from the start. This spacious new build is perfect for groups, individuals or families. The bunkrooms are located around the central courtyard. There is a self-catering kitchen (continental breakfast included). The TV lounge has a log fire and WiFi. Long-term parking, baggage transfer and packed lunches are available on request.

In the heart of the Northumberland International Dark Sky Park and close to the Pennine Way. These striking timber eco-buildings integrate into their natural surroundings making the most of this remarkable location and providing the perfect base for outdoor adventures.

The bunkhouse and bothies provide stylish, versatile & comfortable self-catering accommodation which can be used for events, conferences & parties.

DETAILS

- **Open** - All year. Arrive after 3.30pm depart by 10am.
- **Beds** - 22: 1x5, 3x4, 1x3, 1x2.
- **Price/night** - B&B from £35-£40 (adult) Group discounts.

DETAILS

- **Open** - Mid January - December.
- **Beds** - 52: Bunkhouse:16-20. Bothies: 4x8. 3 camper van bays.
- **Price/night** - Bunkhouse: £360 to £500. Bothies: £125 to £250.

CONTACT: Mrs Paula Laws
Tel: 01661 854364   or 07708 419911
wjlaws@btconnect.com
www.houghtonnorthfarm.co.uk
Houghton North Farm, Heddon-on-the-Wall, Northumberland, NE15 0EZ

CONTACT: Robert and Claire Cocker
Tel: 01434 240980 or 07891 252801
info@tarset-tor.co.uk
www.tarset-tor.co.uk
Greystones, Lanehead, Tarset, Hexham, NE48 1NT

CHARTNERS FARM
OFF THE GRID
97a

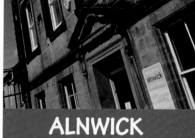

ALNWICK
YOUTH HOSTEL
97b

Hidden away in Harwood Forest, near Rothbury, owned by Forestry England, Chartners Farm is definitely off the grid. It's a 5 mile drive along forest tracks. Electricity is generated by a wind turbine & solar panels, while a huge log burner heats the radiators and keeps the place cosy. The perfect spot to escape the rat race, relax, unwind & recharge or get out into the countryside for energetic walking or biking. Fully equipped for a self-catered break with LPG cooker, microwave, fridge/freezer, radio CD and board games etc.

This family friendly 4* hostel has en suite rooms, cosy lounge, games room and a spacious dining room. Located in the centre of town, it is ideal for Alnwick Castle, (of Downton Abbey and Harry Potter fame) and Alnwick Garden. The coast, with castles at Dunstanburgh and Bamburgh, Farne Isles, magical Holy Island and glorious sandy beaches is just a 15 minute drive. While inland the Cheviot Hills & Hadrian's Wall await you.

      GROUPS ONLY

DETAILS

- **Open** - All year, (subject to weather warnings). Arrival 4pm, departure 11am.
- **Beds** - 12: 2x5,1x2 (bunks and singles)
- **Price/night** - £110 for up to 6 guests; £140 for 7 to 12 guests. Min stay 2 nights.

DETAILS

- **Open** - All year. 8-10am, 4-7pm
- **Beds** - 56:1xdbl,2x2,1x3,6x4,1x5,3x6
- **Price/night** - Peak season: dorm £30. 2 bedded rooms £60. 4 bedded rooms £100. Off-peak: dorm £20. 2 bedded rooms £30. 4 bedded rooms £50.

CONTACT: Nick Davies
chartnersfarm@gmail.com
Chartners, Harwood Forest, Ewesley, Morpeth NE61 4LJ

CONTACT: Reception
Tel: 01665 660800
info@alnwickyouthhostel.co.uk
www.alnwickyouthhostel.co.uk
34 - 38 Green Batt, Alnwick, Northumberland, NE66 1TU

RADCLIFFES
LODGE
98a

Radcliffes Lodge is a purpose-built hostel overlooking the Marina in the vibrant harbour town of Amble on the Northumberland Coast. It sleeps 48 across 9 en suite rooms, has a large open-plan communal area & oozes quality & style. With the Coast & Castles cycle route & the Northumberland Coastal Path on the doorstep, the Lodge is perfect for walkers, cyclists, & groups of friends & families.

DETAILS
- **Open** - All year
- **Beds** - 48: 1x8, 4x6, 4x4 (all private rooms with en suite)
- **Price/night** - Family suites from £140 for 4 people. Bunkbed rooms from £70 for 2 people.

CONTACT: Reception
Tel: 01665 252122 or 07943 682727
info@radcliffeslodge.co.uk
www.coblequay.co.uk
Radcliffes Lodge, Coble Quay, Amble, Northumberland. NE65 0FB

MOUNTHOOLY
BUNKHOUSE
98b

Nestled in the beautiful College Valley, North Northumberland, Mounthooly Bunkhouse is a perfect stop-off on the Pennine Way and St Cuthbert's Way. Dogs are welcome by arrangement. There is a well equipped kitchen and living area with log burner. Bedding, WiFi and car permit (to access this private valley) are provided. A haven for wildlife with red squirrels, otters and a thriving population of feral goats in the valley. The perfect wild get-away from it all.

DETAILS
- **Open** - All year. All day.
- **Beds** - 24: 2x9 1x2 1x4(family)
- **Price/night** - £20pp, £15pp under 18 and concessions. Family room for 4 £70. Sole use £300, £350 (weekends).

CONTACT: Charlene Drysdale
Tel: 01668 216210
mounthooly@college-valley.co.uk
www.college-valley.co.uk
Mount Hooly, College Valley, Wooler, Northumberland, NE71 6TU

ILDERTON
DOD BARNS
99a

WOOLER
YOUTH HOSTEL
99b

Ilderton Dod Barns, in Northumberland National Park, include The Barn, which sleeps 9 in one large sleeping area & Cuckoo Cottage which sleeps 3. On a working hill farm down a 1.5 mile private track. Located close to The Pennine Way and The Sandstone Way with many other footpaths & bridleways on the doorstep. The perfect base for walkers, mountain bikers & horse riders (paddocks available).

Wooler Youth Hostel & Shepherd's Huts are on the edge of the town and offer an ideal base for exploring the Northumberland National Park, the Cheviot Hills, local castles and fine sandy beaches. For walkers there's St Cuthbert's Way and for cyclists, Wooler cycle hub routes, Pennine Cycleway and the Sandstone Way. There are bridleways perfect for mountain biking and lots of bouldering and climbing.

     GROUPS ONLY

DETAILS
- **Open** - All year.
- **Beds** - 12: The Barn 9: 4xsgl, 2xbunk, 1xdbl + camp bed. Cottage 3: 1xsgl, 1xdbl
- **Price/night** - The Barn: £406 - £713 (up to 3 nights), £529 - £930 (7 nights). Cottage: £292-463 / £380-604.

DETAILS
- **Open** - March-Oct. (Group bookings Nov to Feb). Reception 8-10am & 5-8pm.
- **Beds** - 51: 4x2, 5x4, 1x6, 1x8. Shepherd's Huts 3x2, 1x3 (family).
- **Price/night** - From £22 adult, £20 child. Group discounts available.

CONTACT: Pam or Robert
Tel: 0778 6253793 or 0793 2782611
ildertondodbarns@hotmail.com
www.ildertondodbarns.co.uk
The Dod, Powburn, Alnwick,
Northberland NE66 4JL

CONTACT: Hostel Manager
Tel: 01668 281365
hello@woolerhostel.co.uk
www.woolerhostel.co.uk
30 Cheviot Street, Wooler,
Northumberland, NE71 6LW

CHATTON PARK
BUNKHOUSE
100a

A former smithy converted into a self-catering bunkhouse on a mixed working farm 1/2 mile from Chatton. Eight miles from Northumberland's vast empty beaches and historic castles and five miles from the heather clad Cheviot Hills.

Walking, water sports, climbing, fishing, golf and cycling are all nearby. Fully equipped kitchen, seating around the original blacksmith's fire & hot showers.

DETAILS

- **Open** - March to November. Flexible times but no check in after 9pm.
- **Beds** - 8: 2x4
- **Price/night** - From £175 sole use. Teens must be led by a responsible adult. Dogs: £10/dog/stay.

CONTACT: Jane or Duncan
Tel: 01668 215765 or 07825 046008
jaord@btinternet.com
www.chattonparkfarm.co.uk
Chatton Park Farm, Chatton, Alnwick, Northumberland, NE66 5RA

BLUEBELL
FARM BUNKBARN
100b

Bluebell Farm Bunkbarn is within walking distance of shops and pubs. It is ideally located for exploring Nothumberland's Heritage Coast, the Cheviot Hills and the Scottish Borders. The Bunkbarn sleeps 14, the Studio 4. Plus 2 studio apartments and 5 self-catering cottages. There is a shared modern toilet block. BYO sleeping bags/towels or hire. Studio apartments & cottages have bed linen.

DETAILS

- **Open** - All year. Check in by 9 pm, departure by 10 am.
- **Beds** - 18: Bunkbarn 14: 1x8, 1x6. Studio 4: 1x4. Plus apartments & cottages
- **Price/night** - Bunkbarn: £20, under 16s £10. Studio: £25, under 16s £12.50. Linen and towel hire £8pp. Sole use rates available.

CONTACT: Phyl
Tel: 01668 213362
corillas@icloud.com
Bluebell Farm Caravan Park, Belford, Northumberland, NE70 7QE

SEAHOUSES
HOSTEL
101a

Within easy walking distance of Seahouses, this recently refurbished hostel offers affordable, spacious & comfortable accommodation. A perfect base for visiting the beaches and castles of the Northumbrian Coast. Particularly popular with divers, families, cyclists, walkers, school, church and youth groups. Groups of all sizes welcome. Sole use available. Booking essential.

DETAILS

■ **Open** - All year. Arrive after 4pm, depart by 10am unless otherwise agreed.
■ **Beds** - 42: 1x10, 1x8, 1x6, 1x6 (en suite wet room), 2x4, 2×2 (en suite),
■ **Price/night** - Recognised youth groups £19pp. Adults £24 to £30pp; children £19pp; under 5s free. Min 2 nights.

CONTACT: Karen Leadbitter
Tel: 07531 305206
seahouseshostel@outlook.com
www.seahouseshostel.org.uk
157 Main Street, Seahouses,
Northumberland NE68 7TU

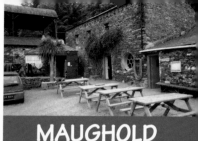

MAUGHOLD
VENTURE CENTRE
101b

Maughold Venture Centre Bunkhouse overlooks farmland with views out to sea. The popular beach of Port e Vullen is just 10 min's walk away. Enjoy self-catering accommodation, with en suite, centrally heated rooms. Tasty meals are available from the neighbouring Venture Centre, where you can also book kayaking, abseiling, air rifle shooting, archery, gorge walking, dinghy sailing & team events. With its own stop, Lewaigue Halt, on the Manx Electric Railway you have easy access to Douglas, Ramsey, mountains & tranquil glens.

DETAILS

■ **Open** - January - December. 24 hours.
■ **Beds** - 52: 2x2, 1x5, 4x8, 2x10.
■ **Price/night** - £20 per person.

CONTACT: Simon Read
Tel: 01624 814240
contact@adventure-centre.co.uk
www.venturecentre.im
The Venture Centre, Maughold, Isle of
Man, IM7 1AW

South Wales

| 0 | miles | 25 |
| 0 | kilometres | 40 |

124b

123a
124a

Aberystwyth

New Quay

A487

Cardigan

Lampeter

118a

117b
Fishguard

118b

117a
116b
St Davids

Carmarthen

Haverfordwest   A40   **St Clears**

114b

116a

115b

Pembroke   **Tenby**   **Llanelli**

115a

114a
113b
113a 112b

KEY

45 -   **Page number**

45a -   **Left side of page**

45b -   **Right side of page**

45 -   **Groups only**

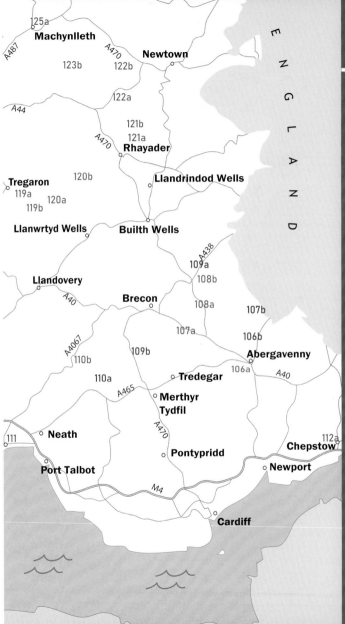

South Wales

125a
Machynlleth
A487
A470
Newtown
123b
122b
122a
A44
121b
121a
A470
Rhayader
120b
Tregaron
119a
120a
119b
Llandrindod Wells
Llanwrtyd Wells
Builth Wells
A438
Llandovery
A40
109a
108b
Brecon
108a
107b
107a
106b
A4067
Abergavenny
110b
109b
106a
A40
Tredegar
110a
A465
Merthyr
Tydfil
A470
Neath
111
112a
Chepstow
Pontypridd
Port Talbot
Newport
M4
Cardiff

ENGLAND

North Wales

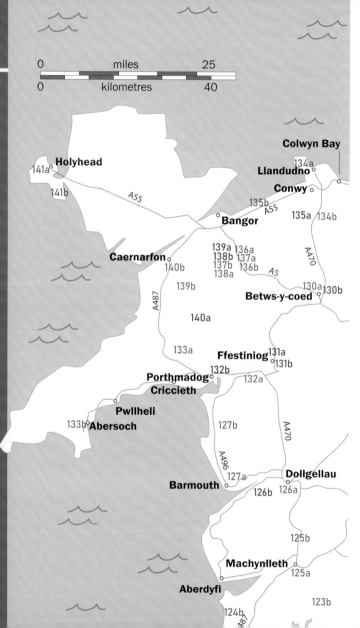

0   miles   25
0   kilometres   40

Colwyn Bay
134a
Llandudno
Conwy
135b
A55
135a   134b
Holyhead
141a
141b
A55
Bangor
A470
Caernarfon
139a 136a
138b 137a
137b 136b
138a
A5
140b
139b
130a 130b
Betws-y-coed
A487
140a
133a
Ffestiniog 131a
131b
132b
Porthmadog
132a
Criccieth
Pwllheli
127b
A470
133b **Abersoch**
A496
127a
Barmouth
Dollgellau
126b 126a
125b
Machynlleth
125a
Aberdyfi
123b
124b
487

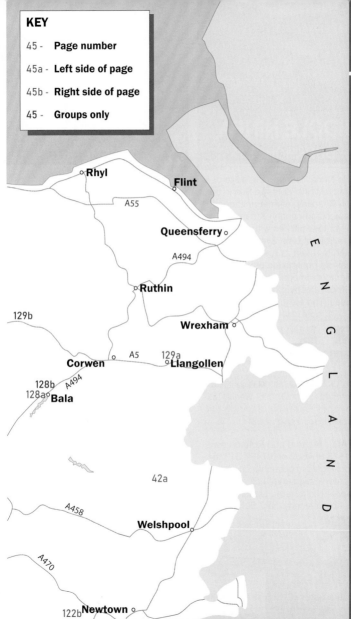

KEY

45 - **Page number**

45a - **Left side of page**

45b - **Right side of page**

45 - **Groups only**

Rhyl

Flint

A55

Queensferry

A494

Ruthin

129b

Wrexham

Corwen   A5   129a
                  Llangollen

128b
128a Bala   A494

42a

A458

Welshpool

A470

122b Newtown

ENGLAND

North Wales

MIDDLE NINFA
BUNKHOUSE
106a

Middle Ninfa Farm, on the edge of Blaenavon World Heritage Site in the Brecon Beacons, offers bunkhouse/cottage accommodation & camping on eleven 'remote' pitches with fine views over the Vale of Usk. Sympathetically renovated to retain its rustic charm, the 400-year-old bunkhouse provides self-catering accommodation for 6 people. BYO food, sleeping bags, towels & pillowcases. The electric heating may be cool in winter.

DETAILS
- **Open** - All year.
- **Beds** - 6: 1x4, 1x2 (dbl) plus camping.
- **Price/night** - From £13pp. Weekly rate for 6 persons £430-480. Camping (inc hammocks) £6 pp + pitch fee of £6/£12.

CONTACT: Richard and Rohan Lewis
Tel: 01873 854662 or 07497 818354
bookings@middleninfa.co.uk
www.middleninfa.co.uk
Middle Ninfa Farm, Llanellen,
Abergavenny, NP7 9LE

SMITHYS
BUNKHOUSE
106b

Smithy's Bunkhouse accommodates groups of up to 24 in two dormitories of 12 bunks.

Located on a working farm just outside Abergavenny in the Brecon Beacons, there are great walking/running and cycling routes from the doorstep.

A range of outdoor activities can be organised if required. There's a traditional pub serving bar snacks and meals at the end of the drive for the times you don't want to self-cater.

DETAILS
- **Open** - All year
- **Beds** - 24 : 2x12 + camping
- **Price/night** - From £18pp

CONTACT: Tracey
Tel: 07482 226103 or 07885 257788
tracey@smithysbunkhouse.net
www.smithysbunkhouse.net
Lower House Farm, Pantygelli,
Abergavenny, Monmouthshire, NP7 7HR

THE STAR
BUNKHOUSE
107a

THE WAIN HOUSE
107b

Ideal base for exploring the Brecon Beacons National Park. Situated in the village of Bwlch alongside the Beacons Way long distance footpath. Expect a warm and comfortable stay in a dog friendly bunkhouse with spacious bedrooms, lounge/dining areas, self-catering kitchen, BBQ, hot showers, drying room and off-road parking. Accommodation for up to 20 people over 6 bedrooms. Private bedrooms or sole use available for individuals, couples & groups.

This old stone barn continues the tradition of 900 years when Llanthony Priory next door provided accommodation. Surrounded by the Black Mountains in the Brecon Beacons National Park, it is your ideal base for all mountain activities. There is a fully equipped kitchen, hot showers, heating throughout and a wood burning stove. Small or large groups are welcome with sole use and a minimum charge. Two pubs nearby offer real ale and bar food.

DETAILS

- **Open** - All year. All day.
- **Beds** - 20: 1x4/5 (en-suite), 3x4, 2x2
- **Price/night** - Private rooms from £22. Sole use from £280.

DETAILS

- **Open** - All year. All day. No restrictions.
- **Beds** - 16: 1x8, 1x4, 1x6.
- **Price/night** - £40 per person for a two-night weekend, with a minimum charge of £400. Mid-week reductions.

CONTACT: Emma & Peter Harrison
Tel: 01874 730080 or 07341 906937
info@starbunkhouse.com
www.starbunkhouse.com
Brecon Road (A40), Bwlch, Brecon,
Powys, LD3 7RQ

CONTACT: Cordelia Passmore
Tel: 01873 890359
courtfarm@llanthony.co.uk
www.llanthonybunkbarn.co.uk
Court Farm, Llanthony, Abergavenny,
Monmouthshire, NP7 7NN

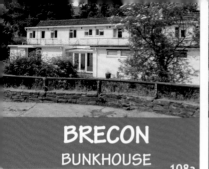

BRECON
BUNKHOUSE
108a

108b
LIVING ENERGY
BUNKHOUSE

Brecon Bunkhouse is a spacious, comfortable, accommodation in the Brecon Beacons. It is a great value, self-catering accommodation with a big dining room and sitting room with wood-burner.

In the Black Mountains, with mountain walks from the door, an ideal base for horse riding, mountain biking and canoeing. There is a riding centre on the farm and the bunkhouse has a drying room and storage/cleaning facilities for bikes and canoes. Camping available.

Formerly known as Cadarn Bunkhouse, The Living Energy Bunkhouse, run by Living Energy Holidays, will be open from April 2023.

Situated on a small hill farm in the Brecon Beacons. with easy access to mountains & the river Wye, it is perfect for walking, mountain biking, horse riding & canoeing.

DETAILS

- **Open** - April to Nov & New Year
- **Beds** - 14: Tack Barn 7: 1x3, 2x2. Bunkhouse 3: 1x3. Cottage 4: 2x2.
- **Price/night** - Tack Barn/Bunkhouse: from £22pp. Cottage: from £30pp. Min occupancy 2 people. Special rates for sole use. Breakfast: £6.50-£12

DETAILS

- **Open** - All year. All day.
- **Beds** - 28: 1x10, 1x8, 1x6, 2x2,
- **Price/night** - £20pp, minimum of 4 people. £300 for exclusive use.

CONTACT: Paul and Emily Turner
breconbunkhouse@gmail.com
www.brecon-bunkhouse.co.uk
Brecon Bunkhouse, Cwmfforest Farm, Pengenfford, Talgarth, Brecon, LD3 0EU

CONTACT: Lynette Avis
Tel: 07774 145479 or 01497 847103
LCFholidays@yahoo.com
www.livingenergyholidays.co.uk
Lower Cwmcadarn Farm, Felindre, Three Cocks, Brecon, Powys, LD3 0TB

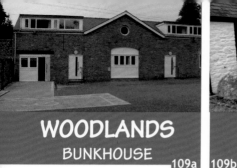

WOODLANDS
BUNKHOUSE
109a

Woodlands Bunkhouse is a converted stable block set in the 10 acre grounds of Woodlands Centre. It overlooks the River Wye and has wonderful views of the Black Mountains. The historic town of Hay on Wye is near by. The Bunkhouse provides comfortable, modern accommodation for families and groups, with availability at weekends and during school holidays. There's a well equipped kitchen and dining room and 22 beds in 9 rooms. The bunkhouse can arrange courses in a variety of outdoor activities.

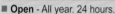

DETAILS
- **Open** - All year. 24 hours.
- **Beds** - 22 in 9 rooms of 1 to 6 plus camping in the grounds.
- **Price/night** - £16 pp + VAT. Reduction for children and large group bookings.

CONTACT: Chris Pierce
Tel: 01497 847272
chris.pierce@oxfordshireoutdoors.co.uk
www.oxfordshireoutdoorlearningservice.co.uk
Glasbury on Wye, Powys, HR3 5LP

COED OWEN
BUNKHOUSE
109b

Set on a hill farm in the heart of the Brecon Beacons, 2 hours' walk from Pen Y Fan. This Bunkhouse provides well appointed self-catering accommodation; ideal for stag, hen and family parties. Outdoor activities can be organised or there's direct access onto the mountains and waterfalls close by. Bike Park Wales, Merthyr Tydfil, Penderyn Whisky and Brecon are all within easy reach. The pub at the bottom of the drive serves great food and fine ales.

DETAILS
- **Open** - All year. All day.
- **Beds** - 26: 2x6, 1x10, 1 dbl, 1 twin.
- **Price/night** - From £25 per person per night with bed linen. Min of two nights at weekends. Min of 18 people.

CONTACT: Molly or Netty Rees
Tel: 07508 544044
info@breconbeaconsbunkhouse.co.uk
www.breconbeaconsbunkhouse.co.uk
Coed Owen Farm, Cwmtaff, Merthyr Tydfil, CF48 2HY

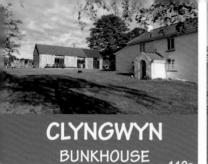

CLYNGWYN
BUNKHOUSE
110a

Clyngwyn Farm offers exclusive use of the Bunkhouse for group accommodation, sleeping 19. Minutes away from waterfalls & the best walking in the Brecon Beacons. New fully equipped kitchen, big lounge, wifi and central heating provides the perfect year round stay. 3 bedrooms, 14 single beds and two sets of bunks. Outside fire pit & undercover bbq area. Catering available & organising outdoor activities if required. Camping facilities.

         GROUPS ONLY

DETAILS

- **Open** - All year
- **Beds** - 19: Bunkhouse, plus camping.
- **Price/night** - Sun-Thurs £425, Fri/Sat £495. Bank holidays £550. Min 2 night stay (3 at Bank hols). Camping £10pp.

CONTACT: Linda Williams
Tel: 01639 722930
stay@clyngwyn.co.uk
www.bunkhouse-south-wales.co.uk
Clyngwyn Farm, Ystradfellte Rd,
Pontneddfechan, Powys, SA11 5US

CRAIG Y NOS
CASTLE
110b

Craig Y Nos Castle sits in the Brecon Beacons. The Nurses Block can be booked on a daily or a room basis. It can also be booked sole use as group accommodation. Offering B&B or self-catering, the choice is yours. The castle provides hearty meals, cosy evenings by the wood burning stoves and a free history tour. Superior B&B rooms are available in the castle.

DETAILS
- **Open** - All year
- **Beds** - Nurses Block: 21: 10x2, 1x1. Castle: 67 rooms: (64 en suite)
- **Price/night** - B&B £70 per twin bed room. Sole use of Bunkhouse: 1 night £350, 2 nights £500, 3 nights £600, 5 nights £700.

CONTACT: Reception
Tel: 01639 730725
info@craigynoscastle.com
www.craigynoscastle.com
Craig Y Nos Castle, Brecon Road,
Penycae, Powys, SA9 1GL

CWTSH
HOSTEL
111a

CWTSH
HOSTEL
111b

Cwtsh hostel is new, exciting and trend-setting. Situated in the heart of Swansea City Centre, overlooking Castle Gardens, Cwtsh Hostel provides a modern and unique base to explore the city and surrounding areas.

Choose from pod-bunk or private accommodation. Electric bike hire and introductory Welsh classes - bendigedig available. Backpackers, explorers, families, party-goers, schools and freelancers are all welcomed.

Mae Hostel Cwtsh yn newydd, cyffrous ac unigryw. Wedi'i leoli yng nghanol Abertawe.

Yn Ganol y Ddinas, yn edrych dros Sgwâr y Castell,Mae Hostel Cwtsh yn darparu gwasanaeth modern, perffaith i grwydro'r ddinas a'r ardaloedd cyfagos. Dewiswch o pod neu stafell breifat. Llogwch feiciau trydan a mynychu dosbarthiadau Cymraeg - bendigedig. Backpackers, teuluoedd, ysgolion, grwpiau mae 'na groeso i bawb!

DETAILS	MANYLION
■ **Open** - All year	■ **Agored** - Trwy'r flwyddyn
■ **Beds** - 54	■ **Gwelyau** - 54
■ **Price/night** - Pod-bunk beds from £20. Private rooms from £50.	■ **Pris/nos** - Gwelyau pod-bync o £20. Ystafelloedd preifat o £50.

CONTACT: Llyr Roberts
Tel: 01792 986556
hello@cwtsh-hostel.co.uk
www.cwtsh-hostel.co.uk
10-14 Castle St, Swansea SA1 1JF

CONTACT: Llyr Roberts
Tel: 01792 986556
hello@cwtsh-hostel.co.uk
www.cwtsh-hostel.co.uk
10-14 Castle St, Swansea SA1 1JF

GREEN MAN
BACKPACKERS
112a

EASTERN SLADE
BARN
112b

Green Man Backpackers offers inspired accommodation in a Grade ll building in the heart of Chepstow. Chepstow is the starting/finishing point for Offa's Dyke path, the Wales Coast Path, Gloucester Way and the Wye Valley Walk. The Land's End/John O'Groats route is just 1 mile away. The Forest of Dean & Wye Valley AONB are also nearby.

Eastern Slade Barn is a luxury farmhouse conversion on a working farm on the Gower Peninsula. The Gower has glorious beaches, castles and traffic free lanes. The coast path passes through the farm. Port Eynon seaside village is a 30 min walk, while Oxwich Bay with its castle, beach & hotel serving tasty meals is just 20 mins walk. Camping available and weddings/birthdays welcome.

DETAILS

- **Open** - All year. All day. Except Christmas to New Year's Eve/Day.
- **Beds** - 40: 28 in dorms of 6 or 4 beds, 5 en suite family / twin rooms.
- **Price/night** - Dorms from £30pp, family/4 bed rooms from £65 (en suite from £75), 5 bed from £100, family/double en suite (sleeps 3) from £110.

DETAILS

- **Open** - All year. 24 hours.
- **Beds** - 15: 1x5, 2x2/3 (double with bunk above), 1x2, 2 in lounge
- **Price/night** - Low season: £20pp, £200 sole use, 2 nights min. High season: £25pp, £260 sole use, 3 nights min. £30 cleaning charge .

CONTACT: Kim and Jon
Tel: 07773 553397 or 01291 626773
info@greenmanbackpackers.co.uk
greenmanbackpackers.co.uk
13 Beaufort Square, Chepstow, NP16 5EP (Car park NP16 5LL)

CONTACT: Kate
Tel: 07970 969814
tynrheol@hotmail.com
easternsladebarngower.co.uk
Eastern Slade Farm, Oxwich, Gower, Swansea, SA3 1NA

RHOSSILI
BUNKHOUSE
113a

HARDINGSDOWN
BUNKHOUSE
113b

Rhossili 4* Bunkhouse is situated at the end of the Gower Peninsula, in the first Area of Outstanding Natural Beauty. It is within easy walking distance of three glorious beaches, (including Rhossili Bay which has been voted the best beach in Europe & in the top ten in the World). Ideal for families & groups, it is perfectly located for a wide range of outdoor activities including walking, surfing, paddle boarding, cycling & climbing.

GROUPS ONLY

DETAILS
■ **Open** - All year except January. Check in 4-9pm. Check out by 10:30am.
■ **Beds** - 22: 1x4, 2x3, 4x2. + 4 sofa-beds in lounge (sole use).
■ **Price/night** - Full (group of 18) £450. Sole (group of 22) £495.

CONTACT: Josephine Higgins
Tel: 01792 391509
manager@rhossilibunkhouse.com
www.rhossilibunkhouse.com
Rhossili Bunkhouse, Rhossili, Swansea, SA3 1PL

Hardingsdown Bunkhouse and The Chaffhouse both provide accommodation for families or groups.
Comfortable and well appointed they are perfect for exploring Gower and all it has to offer. The properties can be hired individually or together. Rates vary with numbers.

DETAILS
■ **Open** - All year. All day.
■ **Beds** - 22: Bunkhouse 12: 1x5, 1x3, 2x2. Chaffhouse: 10: 1x4 3x2
■ **Price/night** - Hardingsdown Bunkhouse: (12 people max) £220. The Chaffhouse: (10 people max) £220. Midweek. £200. Enquire for rates for both units together. Weekly rates available. INDIVIDUALS mid week only, £35pp.

CONTACT: Allison Tyrrell
Tel: 01792 386222
bunkhousegower@btconnect.com
www.bunkhousegower.co.uk
Lower Hardingsdown Farm, Llangennith, Gower, Swansea, SA3 1HT

ST MADOC
CENTRE
114a

PANTYRATHRO
INTERNATIONAL HOSTEL
114b

Situated on the Gower Peninsular, St Madoc Centre offer superb facilities for groups of between 40 and 81. Set in 76 acres of fields, woodland, headland and coastline, with tennis & volleyball courts, playing fields and a campfire area, it is ideally suited to schools, youth & church groups, corporate events, weddings and friends & family get-togethers. Optional outdoor activities and catered packages available for school groups.

Llansteffan is a beautiful village at the tip of the Towi River & Carmarthen Bay. The sandy beaches below the castle offer sun bathing and relaxation. The virtually traffic free country lanes are ideal for cycling. The Wales Coastal Path is on the doorstep and the city of Carmarthen is close by. The hostel provides private rooms, family rooms and en suite rooms.

DETAILS

DETAILS
- **Open** - All year
- **Beds** - 81: 2x2, 2x4, 1x5, 4x10, 2x12. Mostly en suite.
- **Price/night** - From £21pp. Youth groups from £17.50. Min group size 40, 60 in summer.

DETAILS
- **Open** - February to January. 24 hours.
- **Beds** - 43: 1x10, 1x8, 1x6, 3x4, 1x3, 2x2
- **Price/night** - Private rooms: twin/double £45 each. 4 bed rooms available privately for 1,2,3, or 4 people. Priced from £20 per person enquire for details. Groups welcome.

CONTACT: Heather Lyne
Tel: 01792 386291
info@stmadoc.co.uk
www.stmadoc.co.uk/
LLanmadoc, Gower, Swansea,
SA3 1DE.

CONTACT: Ken Knuckles
Tel: 01267 241721 or 01267 241014
kenknuckles@hotmail.com
www.backpackershostelwales.com
Pantyrathro International Hostel,
Llansteffan, Carmarthen, SA33 5AJ

STACKPOLE
CENTRE
115a

The 121-bed, Stackpole Centre is the perfect venue for large families/groups, schools, special interest breaks and outdoor activities.

Close to wild woodlands and stunning beaches. It comprises four large group houses, 2 of which are dog friendly. Book by the house or book the whole centre for your sole use.

     GROUPS ONLY

DETAILS
- **Open** - All year. All day. Reception 9-5.
- **Beds** - 117: Kingfisher: 10 b/rooms (44 guests). Kestrel: 13 b/rooms (38 guests). Swan: 13 b/rooms (24 guests). Shearwater: 7 b/rooms (15 guests).
- **Price/night** - Whole site £2500, Kingfisher £834, Kestrel £510, Swan £714, Shearwater £390.

CONTACT: Stackpole Reception
Tel: 01646 623 110
stackpole.bookings@nationaltrust.org.uk
The Old Home Farm Yard, Stackpole, nr
Pembroke, Pembrokeshire, SA71 5DQ

UPPER NEESTON
LODGES
115b

Environmentally sensitive barn conversions close to the Milford Haven Waterway in the Pembrokeshire Coast National Park. Ideal for divers, climbers, walkers or family get-togethers. The four independent 5* lodges have fully fitted kitchens and have access to garden/ patio, laundry/drying room, secure storage and ample parking.

DETAILS
- **Open** - All year. Check in from 4pm. Check out before 10.30am.
- **Beds** - 24: Cowshed 10: 1x6,1x4. Barn 8: 1x6,1x2, Granary 1x3. Dairy 1x3
- **Price/night** - From £17.50 (inc linen). Min 2 nights at w/ends (3 nights b/h). Sole use: min 6 Barn, 8 Cowshed. Smaller groups/individuals by agreement.

CONTACT: Sean or Mandy Tilling
Tel: 01646 690750
mail@upperneeston.co.uk
www.upperneeston.co.uk
Upper Neeston Farm, Dale Road,
Herbrandston, Milford Haven, SA73 3RY

SKOMER
ISLAND HOSTEL
116a

Staying overnight on Skomer Island provides the perfect chance to get away from the hustle and bustle of everyday life. You'll be one of a maximum of 16-overnight guests staying in the 3-star hostel accommodation, nestled at the very heart of the island. With so few people, there's always a quiet place or an amazing wildlife encounter just round the corner. Beautiful, peaceful, and entirely unforgettable.

DETAILS
- **Open** - 1st April - 30th September
- **Beds** - 16: 1x5, 1x4, 1x3, 2x2
- **Price/night** - April - £60pp. May/June/July - £85pp. August/September - £50pp. Children 12 and under are half price.

CONTACT: Booking office
Tel: 01656 724100
islands@welshwildlife.org
www.welshwildlife.org/skomer-island-overnight-stays
Skomer Island, Martins Haven, Haverfordwest, SA62 3BJ.

CAERHAFOD
LODGE
116b

Situated between the famous cathedral city of St Davids and the Irish ferry port of Fishguard, the 4* Lodge overlooks the spectacular Pembrokeshire coastline. Within walking distance of the Sloop Inn at Porthgain and the internationally renowned Coastal Path. An ideal stopover for cyclists with The Celtic Trail cycle route passing the bottom of the drive. The lodge sleeps 23 in 5 separate rooms, all en suite with great showers. Dogs welcome by arrangement.

DETAILS
- **Open** - All year. Check in from 5pm, check out 10.30 am. All day access.
- **Beds** - 23: 3x4, 1x5, 1x6.
- **Price/night** - Adult £25. Under 16s £20. Min 2 nights. Sole use hire available.

CONTACT: Carolyn Rees
Tel: 01348 837859
Caerhafod@aol.com
www.caerhafod.co.uk
Llanrhian, St Davids, Haverfordwest, Pembrokeshire, SA62 5BD

OLD SCHOOL
HOSTEL
117a

THE HAMILTONS
117b

Escape to this wonderful rugged corner of the Pembrokeshire Coast National Park. Old School Hostel is in Trefin, a pretty village which has a pub and a café, just a quarter of a mile from the world famous coast path. Circular walks from the door take you to stunning wild beaches & harbours. The cathedral city of St. Davids and the popular Whitesands Bay are 20 minutes by car.

Hamilton Lodge and James John Hamilton House sit side by side in the coastal town of Fishguard close to the Pembrokeshire Coastal Path. They provide B&B rooms, a holiday cottage and quality self-catering accommodation for groups of up to 20 people.

Fishguard is a natural harbor surrounded by the sweeping sands of Cardigan Bay, regularly visited by communities of grey seals and dolphins.

DETAILS

■ **Open** - All year, but we strongly advise you check availability first.
■ **Beds** - 22: 1x6, 3x2, 2x2/3 (bunk with dbl lower bed), 1x4 (1 dbl + 1 bunk). Single occupancy available.
■ **Price/night** - From £40. Single occ from £40. Sole use from £350.

DETAILS

■ **Open** - All year
■ **Beds** - 20: James John 12: 2x twin, 2xdbl, 1x4 (family). Hamilton Lodge 8: 1x4, 1xtwin, 1xdbl.
■ **Price/night** - Please enquire for prices.

CONTACT: Paul
Tel: 0784 562 5005
paul.moger@gmail.com
oldschoolhostel.com
Ffordd-yr-Afon, Trefin, Haverfordwest, Pembrokeshire, SA62 5AU

CONTACT: Quentin or Steve
Tel: 07505 562939 or 07813 687570
hamiltonlodgefishguard@gmail.com
www.hamiltonlodgefishguard.co.uk
19a and 23 Hamilton Street, Fishguard, Pembrokeshire SA65 9HL

THE LONG BARN

118a

GILFACH WEN
BARN

118b

Penrhiw is an organic farm with views over the Teifi Valley. The stunning Ceredigion Coast and the Cambrian Mountains are an easy drive away and the busy small town of Llandysul (1.5 miles) has all essential supplies. The farm's location is ideal for exploring, studying or simply admiring the Welsh countryside. Local activities include swimming, climbing, abseiling, canoeing, farm walks and cycling.

A homely, high quality, bunkhouse for individuals, extended families or groups on a working farm. The large social area is ideal for reunions or celebrations. There are 7 family bedrooms including one downstairs for disabled.

Perfect for exploring Carmarthenshire, Pembrokeshire, Brecon Beacons, Cambrian Mountains and the Gower. Walker, cyclist, dog & equestrian friendly.

Village pub close by.

DETAILS

- **Open** - All year. All day.
- **Beds** - 43: Long Barn 31: 1x15, 1x14, 1x2. Cowshed: 6:1x6. Annex 3: 1x3 (dbl+sgl). Cwtch 3: 1x3 (dbl+sofa bed)
- **Price/night** - £20pp. Discount for groups and mid-week bookings.

CONTACT: Tom or Eva
Tel: 01559 363200 or 07733 026874
cowcher@thelongbarn.co.uk
www.thelongbarn.co.uk
Penrhiw, Capel Dewi, Llandysul,
Ceredigion, SA44 4PG

DETAILS

- **Open** - All year. All day.
- **Beds** - 32: 3x6,1x5,1x4,1x3,1x2. Total 10 double & 12 singles in 7 bedrooms.
- **Price/night** - From £19.50pp

CONTACT: Jillie
Tel: 07780 476737
info@gilfachwenbarn.co.uk
www.gilfachwenbarn.co.uk
Gilfach Wen, Brechfa, Carmarthenshire,
SA32 7QL

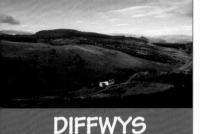

DIFFWYS
OUTDOOR CENTRE
119a

Diffwys Outdoor Centre offers self-catered accommodation for up to 16 people looking to enjoy the remote and tranquil area of the Cambrian Mountains. Intersected by a range of walking and cycling trails, gentle woodlands, tumbling waterfalls and secluded lakes and rivers, this stunning area is perfect for any lover of the great outdoors. With a vast range of peaceful sandy beaches, rocky bays and cliff top walks this undiscovered area of Wales truly has it all.

DETAILS

- **Open** - All year
- **Beds** - 16: 1x12, 2x2 (ensuite).
- **Price/night** - From: ensuite rooms (2 guests) £50. Dorm (12 guests) £240. Whole centre (16 guests) £320.

CONTACT: Sasha
Tel: 01974 298486
bookings@diffwys.co.uk
www.diffwys.co.uk
Diffwys Outdoor Centre, Tregaron, Ceredigion, SY25 6NN

TYNCORNEL
HOSTEL
119b

Tyncornel is a former farmhouse set in stunning Cambrian Mountain scenery at the head of the beautiful Doethie Valley. It is one of the most remote hostels in Wales, favoured by walkers cyclists, and birdwatchers. The hostel sleeps 16. There is a cosy common room with wood-burning stove, two dormitories with built-in bunk beds and a self-catering kitchen. Shepherd's Hut available for spring 2023. On the Cambrian Way.

DETAILS

- **Open** - All year. Reception 5pm -11pm, 7am -10am.
- **Beds** - 16: 2x8.
- **Price/night** - £15, £7 (under 18s). Private rooms available. Whole hostel £210. Campers £10. Shepherd's Hut £85.

CONTACT: Janet or Richard
Tel: 01980 629259 or 07943 091941
Tyncornel.bookings@btinternet.com
www.elenydd-hostels.co.uk
Llanddewi Brefi, Tregaron, Ceredigion, SY25 6PH

DOLGOCH
HOSTEL
120a

CWM CLYD
BUNKHOUSE
120b

Experience the peace of the remote Tywi valley in an era before electricity at this 17th century farmhouse. Dolgoch is a traditional simple hostel owned by the Elenydd Wilderness Trust. It has hot showers, log burner, self-catering kitchen, dormitories & private rooms. The Lôn Las Cymru and the Cambrian Way pass nearby and there are many mountain tracks to explore. Ideal for bird-watchers and lovers of the solitude of the scenic Cambrian Mountains.

Nestling in the Elan Valley in Mid Wales, Cwm Clyd Bunkhouse offers comfortable accommodation in an idyllically remote location. Sleeping 21 across 2 units, which can be booked separately or together, it is ideal for lovers of the great outdoors. After a busy day the star spangled sky of the Elan Valley Dark Sky Park is your evening entertainment. Dogs welcome with sole use bookings.

DETAILS

- **Open** - All year
- **Beds** - 21: Longhouse 14: 1x6, 1x5, 1x3. Carthouse 6: 1x4, 1x2 . Plus 1 accessible en suite room
- **Price/night** - £20 pp. Longhouse: min £180. Whole unit £265. Carthouse: min £80. Whole unit £115. Accessible room £15. Sole use of both units: £260-£350.

DETAILS

- **Open** - All year. 24 hours. Reception 5pm -10pm, 8am -10am.
- **Beds** - 20: 3 rooms inc private rooms.
- **Price/night** - £15 per adult, £7.50 (under 18). 4 bed room £55. 6 bed room £80. Whole hostel £250. Campers £10.

CONTACT: Gillian Keen
Tel: 01440 730226
dolgoch.bookings@elenydd-hostels.co.uk
www.elenydd-hostels.co.uk
Tregaron, Ceredigion, SY25 6NR

CONTACT: Sam Price
Tel: 01597 810449
stay@elanvalley.org.uk
www.elanvalley.org.uk
Claerwen Valley, Rhayader, LD6 5HF

BEILI NEUADD
BUNKHOUSE
121a

A converted 18th century stone barn in stunning countryside just 2 miles from the small market town of Rhayader, gateway to Elan Valley and the Cambrian Mountains. On three National Cycle routes and the Trans Cambrian Route. Beili Neuadd offers lovely gardens and stunning scenery. The centrally heated barn sleeps 16 in 3 en suite rooms and includes a fully equipped kitchen/dining room and drying room. There is also a self contained annex sleeping 4.

DETAILS
- **Open** - All year. All day.
- **Beds** - Barn 16: 2x6,1x4. Annex: 4 1x4 + 1 chair-bed
- **Price/night** - From £25pp. Sole use from £295.

CONTACT: Ruth Ward
Tel: 07961 210612 or 01597 810211
info@beilineuadd.co.uk
www.beilineuaddaccommodation.co.uk
Beili Neuadd, St Harmon, Rhayader, LD6 5NS

MID WALES
BUNKHOUSE
121b

Mid Wales Bunkhouse has a superb unspoilt rural location, close to the Elan Valley, with a stunning natural garden.

There's walking and biking from the door, and room for your horse. Fully equipped for self-catering. Meals are available on request. Bell tent and camping. Welcomes groups or individuals.

DETAILS
- **Open** - All year. 24 hours. Arrive after 4pm (advise if after 7pm), leave by 11am.
- **Beds** - 26: Bunkhouse 20, plus bell tent & camping
- **Price/night** - £25pp, 6-bed room £125. 14-bed room £260. Sole use of bunkhouse (20 people) £310.

CONTACT: Norma
Tel: 07926 781394 or 07585 998499
norma.leadbetter@icloud.com
www.bunkhousemidwales.co.uk
Woodhouse Farm, St Harmon, Rhayader, LD6 5LY

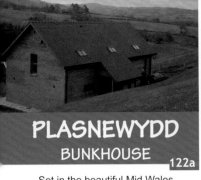

PLASNEWYDD
BUNKHOUSE
122a

BWTHYN
BACH
122b

Set in the beautiful Mid Wales countryside on the Glyndwrs Way, the 4* bunkhouse is an ideal location for exploring or unwinding. Built to the highest standards it provides high quality accommodation for groups or individuals. It can also be booked for conferences and seminars. Attractions close by include sailing, golf course, outdoor pursuit centre, motorbike school and the picturesque market town of Llanidloes (1/2 mile) with many places to eat and drink.

Bwthyn Bach, in the village of Trefeglwys in rural Mid Wales is run by a small trust. Sleeping 17 across 5 rooms, the facilities are simple & add to the quaint & quirky feel of this 300 year old Grade II building.
There's a small kitchen/diner with hot water, kettle, electric cooker, microwave & all the basic crockery/cutlery you will need. A wood-burning Rayburn keeps it warm, while a separate dining room has space for large groups. BYO bedding.

DETAILS

- **Open** - All year.
- **Beds** - 17: 1x6/7, 1x3/4, 1x2/3, 1xdbl, 1xsgl + camping
- **Price/night** - From £20pp plus £40 cleaning fee. Children & Concessions £12pp.

DETAILS

- **Open** - All year. 24 hours. Arrival and departure times by arrangement.
- **Beds** - 27 in 2 dorms + 1 family room.
- **Price/night** - £20pp + £3 for bedding if required. Sole use £403.

CONTACT: Susan
Tel: 01686 412431 or 07975 913049
susanvaughan67@aol.com
www.plasnewyddbunkhouse.co.uk
Gorn Rd, Llanidloes, Powys, SY18 6LA

CONTACT: Amy
Tel: 07975 994164
hello@bwthynbach.com
www.bwthynbach.com
Bwthyn Bach, Trefeglwys, Caersws, Powys. SY17 5QE

PLAS DOLAU
COUNTRY HOUSE HOSTEL
123a

HAFREN FOREST
HIDEAWAY
123b

Plas Dolau is set in 25 acres just 3 miles from Aberystwyth. Ideal for exploring West Wales, walking, cycling, riding, fishing & golf. The mansion has mainly dormitory style accommodation for up to 45. An adjoining Swedish style farmhouse sleeps another 15. Plas Dolau includes meeting rooms, dining rooms, games room & outdoor areas. Suited to youth groups, field courses, retreats, house parties or individuals.

This former weather station has been converted into comfortable accommodation in a quiet location between Llanidloes & Machynlleth in the Cambrian Mountains. A great base for kayaking, mountain biking, fly fishing, family groups & parties.

Fully central heated with a large dining room, well equipped kitchen, comfortable lounge and private bedrooms.

DETAILS
- **Open** - All year. 24 hours.
- **Beds** - 60: Main house: 45:+cots. Farmhouse: 15.
- **Price/night** - From £28 (inc b/fast) to £40 (private, en suite, full b/fast). From £700 whole mansion. From £450 half mansion.

Self catering available for exclusive hire. B&B for individuals or small groups, evening meal available if pre booked.

DETAILS
- **Open** - All year.
- **Beds** - 16: 1x2, 2x4, 1x6.
- **Price/night** - Please enquire for prices.

CONTACT: Pat Twigg
Tel: 01970 617834
sam@plasdolau.co.uk
www.plasdolau.co.uk
Lovesgrove, Aberystwyth, SY23 3HP

CONTACT: Sarah Hackshall
Tel: 07871 740514
info@hafrenforesthideaway.com
hafrenforesthideaway.com
Staylittle, Llanbrynmair, SY19 7DB

ABERYSTWYTH
UNI BUNKHOUSE
124a

BORTH
YOUTH HOSTEL
124b

Aberystwyth University Bunkhouse is on the Wales Coast Path, close to beaches, dramatic walking and white knuckle mountain biking. Aberystwyth has all the attractions of a Victorian seaside town with the added adventure of an ancient castle and thriving nightlife. Accommodation is in single rooms with shared self-catering kitchens and bathrooms. Meals available. Ideal for education trips, conferences or those looking for a base for a family seaside holiday or outdoor group trip.

With 4 miles of stunning beach just 20 metres from the front door, Borth Youth Hostel is perfect for a beach holiday. This Edwardian house has 11 bedrooms and is a great base for visits to the Centre for Alternative Technology, Aberystwyth or the beautiful Dyfi Biosphere. Snowdonia National Park is just a short drive away making Borth perfect for mountain biking, golfing & surfing. The Ceredigion Coast Path passes the door. With two classrooms Borth YH is ideal for school trips. There's free WiFi, a games & TV room, bike storage & drying room. Breakfast, packed lunch & licensed bar.

DETAILS
- **Open** - All year. Reception 9am-5pm.
- **Beds** - 90 Individual bedrooms
- **Price/night** - £36 (2+nights) or £42. Reduced rates for educational groups.

DETAILS
- **Open** - All year. Check in 5pm-10.00pm. Check out 8am-10am
- **Beds** - 60
- **Price/night** - From £18 pp

CONTACT: Conference Office
Tel: 01970 621960
constaff@aber.ac.uk
www.aber.ac.uk/en/visitors/bunkhouse
Penbryn Reception, Aberystwyth
University, Penbryn, Penglais, SY23 3BY

CONTACT: John Taylor
Tel: 01970 871498
john@borthyouthhostel.co.uk
Borth, Ceredigion, Wales, SY24 5JS

TOAD HALL

125a

CORRIS
HOSTEL

125b

Toad Hall sits beside the River Dovey, close to Snowdonia National Park in the market town of Machynlleth. NCN Cycle Route 8 & Glyndwrs Way pass near by.

The accommodation sleeps 9 in a 3-bedroomed self contained unit above the owner's family home. The small flat garden is ideal for camping and there's a small workshop for bike repair/storage.

Perfect for schools, education groups, family celebrations and groups of all kinds, Corris hostel is a haven from the stresses of the outside world with its caring staff & cosy wood fires. Enjoy the gardens with BBQ & campfire areas. Situated in Snowdonia National Park close to Cadair Idris, the Centre for Alternative Technology and just 3 miles from the new Dyfi Bike Park, a mecca for trail bikers. A real paradise for outdoor enthusiasts. CAMRA pub close by.

 GROUPS ONLY

DETAILS

■ **Open** - Not always open, please phone to find out and always pre-book. Please vacate rooms between 12-1pm for cleaning. No arrivals after 11pm please.
■ **Beds** - 8: 1x triple, 1x dbl, 1x twin,1x sgl
■ **Price/night** - £26 pp. Reductions (e.g. for groups) negotiable

DETAILS

■ **Open** - All year by arrangement
■ **Beds** - 43: 1x18, 1x10, 1x6, 1x4, 1x double+2, 1x double+1,
■ **Price/night** - Groups only. Minimum 2 nights, 3 nights Bank Holiday. From £450 per night mid week

CONTACT: Louise
Tel: 01654 700597 or 07779 278188
willcoyn@hotmail.com
Railway Terrace, Doll St, Machynlleth, Powys, SY20 8BH

CONTACT: Michael or Debbie
Tel: 01654 761686
mail@corrishostel.co.uk
Old School, Corris, Machynlleth, Powys, SY20 9TQ

PLAS ISA

126a

KINGS
HOSTEL

126b

In the centre of Dolgellau, Snowdonia, Plas Isa welcomes independent travellers. This Grade II listed building has 5 spacious private bedrooms with 3-5 beds per room. The self-catering kitchen is open for everyone who prefers to cook their own meal. The communal lounge and dining room are great for socialising with your group or other guests. It is the perfect base for active holidays in South Snowdonia for walkers (Cader Idris, Snowdonia Way), mountain bikers (Coed y Brenin) and cyclists (Mawddach Trail, Lon Las Cymru).

Kings Hostel offers groups a uniquely private and affordable place to stay amidst the mountains of Snowdonia. With fabulous walking and cycle routes on the doorstep, a short drive to the coast and all the attractions on the National Park close by, there is something for everyone. Sleeping groups of up to 42 on a sole use basis, this historic hostel is ever popular with schools, clubs and family and friend get-togethers

DETAILS

DETAILS

- **Open** - All year. Check in after 4pm, check out by 10am.
- **Beds** - 19: 2x3, 2x4, 1x5 (no dorms)
- **Price/night** - From £30 per person.

- **Open** - All year. Check in from 4pm. Check out by 10am
- **Beds** - 42: Main building 18: 3x6. Annex 24: 4x6 (all en suite)
- **Price/night** - Sole use £250 to £600 depending on season & length of stay.

CONTACT: Ian and Hanneke
Tel: 01341 423178 or 07984 737066
info@plasisaguesthouse.co.uk
www.plasisaguesthouse.co.uk
Lion Street, Dolgellau, LL40 1DG

CONTACT: Dave Dimmer
Tel: 01341 422392
kings@kingsofsnowdonia.com
www.kingsofsnowdonia.com/
Islawrdref, Dolgellau, LL40 1TB

BUNKORAMA

FFRIDD
BUNKHOUSE

Whether cycling or walking you will love discovering this cosy, clean and comfortable accommodation with breathtaking views of Cader Idris and Cardigan Bay. Handy for Cycle Route 8, the Cambrian Way & Mawddach Trail. Bunkorama is an ideal place to make a stopover or spend a few days exploring the mountains, rivers and beaches of the Cambrian Coast. There is also an adjacent camping pod.

Remote & peaceful, surrounded by the rugged splendour of Snowdonia, Ffridd Bunkhouse offers budget accommodation. Harlech with its beach, pubs, cafes & castle is just 2.5 miles away. This basic accommodation is in 2 units, one sleeps 12 & the other 4/5. Both have kitchen/dining areas & some heating. Each has a separate outside WC, but the shower is shared. Walkers, climbers & mountain bikers alike return annually to this hidden gem of a bunkhouse. BYO bedding.

DETAILS

■ **Open** - All year.
■ **Beds** - 8: 2x4, plus sofa beds in lounge
■ **Price/night** - 4 bed dorm £88 (£96 in winter). If required bedding and towel are £5 and £2 per stay. Discounts available for 2 nights+ and 5nights+

DETAILS

■ **Open** - All year.
■ **Beds** - 18: 1x12, 1x5/6 (4 bunks/1 dbl)
■ **Price/night** - £7pp. Min £28 per night. Discounts for large groups.

CONTACT: Graham
Tel: 07738 467196 or 01341 281134
thebunkorama@gmail.com
www.bunkorama.co.uk
Gwastad Agnes Off Panorama Road,
Barmouth, Gwynedd, LL42 1DX

CONTACT: Wil
Tel: 01766 780329
enquiries@ffridd.org
www.ffridd.org
Ffridd Llwyn Gwerfyl, Harlech, Gwynedd,
LL46 2TW

BALA
BACKPACKERS
128a

BALA
BUNK HOUSE
128b

For outdoor adventures in Snowdonia National Park, Bala Backpackers offers great value 'hostel-style' accommodation, including; 30 comfy SINGLE BEDS in 3,4,5 or 9-bedded rooms. 3 private TWIN ROOMS in a silent-overnight building. Located in a quiet, sunny, chapel square, in the bustling market town of Bala with its five-mile-long lake & white-water river for raft rides.

A converted 200 year old stone building, Bala Bunk House is full of character. Set back from the road in over an acre of grounds with private parking and views of the Berwyn Hills. Ideal for small groups, families & couples. Large patio area with seating, BBQ and fire pit. Close to many outdoor activities. It is the perfect base for walkers & water sport enthusiasts with Bala Lake & the National White Water Centre at the door.

DETAILS

- **Open** - All year by arrangement. 8.30-20.30. Front door locked 00.00 - 6.00am.
- **Beds** - Ask about max: 2x3, 3x4, 3x5 + 3 twin rooms.
- **Price/night** - 1 night £24, 2 nights £45, 3 nights £65, weekly £145. Twin room: £49, en suites from £59. Double holiday-let: £220/4 nights. Sheet hire £3/week.

CONTACT: Stella Shaw
Tel: 01678 521700
info@bala-backpackers.co.uk
www.Bala-Backpackers.co.uk
32 Tegid Street, Bala, LL23 7EL

DETAILS

- **Open** - All year. No restrictions. Telephone 9am - 7pm
- **Beds** - 10: Bunkhouse 8: Cottage 2:
- **Price/night** - Sole use of whole bunkhouse from £240, double annex from £60. Minimum of 2 nights.

CONTACT: Guy and Jane Williams
Tel: 01678 520738
thehappyunion@btinternet.com
www.balabunkhouse.co.uk
Tomen Y Castell, Llanfor, Bala,
Gwynedd, LL23 7HD

LLANGOLLEN
HOSTEL
129a

TYDDYN BYCHAN
129b

Llangollen Hostel, in the Dee Valley, is perfect for walking, cycling, canoeing & white water rafting. Families will love visiting the steam railway, horse drawn canal boats & Pontcysyllte Aqueduct - a World Heritage Site. The town has a great choice of restaurants/pubs and is home to the Fringe music & arts festival, plus the International Eisteddfod. Llandegla, Chester, Wrexham & Offa's Dyke Path are all nearby. A warm welcome awaits!

Tyddyn Bychan is an 18th century Welsh farm surrounded by fields. It is an excellent self-catering base for mountain biking, road cycling, canoeing, walking, climbing, fishing and numerous watersports including white water rafting. The main bunkhouse sleeps 18 in two en suite rooms. All bunks are handmade to a very high standard. The smaller bunkhouse sleeps 9 in two en suite rooms. All bedding is included. Delicious homemade food is available if booked in advance. There is a good parking area well away from the road.

DETAILS

- **Open** - All year. All day.
- **Beds** - 31: 1x6, 1x5, 4x4, 2x2
- **Price/night** - From £20pp for 4 people in a private room. £49 twin/double or £54 en suite. Family of 4 £76, family of 5 £85. Book direct for the best prices.

CONTACT: Sion Dennis
Tel: 01978 861773
info@llangollenhostel.co.uk
www.llangollenhostel.co.uk
Berwyn Street, Llangollen, LL20 8NB

DETAILS

- **Open** - All year. All day.
- **Beds** - 27: 1x10; 1x8; 1x6; 1x3
- **Price/night** - £20 pp including bedding

CONTACT: Lynda Parker
Tel: 01490 420680 or 07523 995741
lynda@tyddynbychan.co.uk
www.tyddynbychan.co.uk
Cefn Brith, Cerrigydrudion, Corwen,
LL21 9TS

VAGABOND
BUNKHOUSE
130a

130b
WOODLANDS
CENTRE

The Vagabond Bunkhouse/Hostel is in the heart of Snowdonia National Park. This unique bunkhouse has been specifically designed for individuals, families or groups.

Very well appointed, it has ready made up beds, free hot drinks, seriously hot showers, a well equipped kitchen & a bar. Catering is available & there is a Pizza restaurant on site (notice required).

Outside there's a climbing wall, a power wash & heated dog kennels!

This large Victorian property has been specially adapted to provide self-catering accommodation for groups of up to 33. The 8 dormitories vary in size from 1 to 10 beds, complete with duvets & linen. The Centre is centrally heated & has a common room, games room, large kitchen, drying room & hot showers. Located in Betws-y-Coed, the Woodlands Centre is an ideal base for outdoor activities in Snowdonia.

DETAILS
- **Open** - All year. Reception open 7.30-10am and 4.30-7.30pm.
- **Beds** - 36: 2x8, 2x6, 2x4
- **Price/night** - £25pp. B&B £31.

DETAILS
- **Open** - All year. All day
- **Beds** - 33: 1x10,1x8,1x4,2x3,2x2,1x1
- **Price/night** - £22.70pp. Sole use: Youth groups £270.82. Adult groups £590.20. Further reductions for members, mid-week bookings & uniformed organisations.

CONTACT: Neil Cawthra
Tel: 01690 710850 or 07816 076546
neilcawthra@mail.com
www.thevagabond.co.uk
Craiglan, Betws-y-Coed, LL24 0AW

CONTACT: Fiona Witton
bookings@woodlandscentre.com
www.woodlandscentre.com
Vicarage Road, Betws-y-Coed, Conwy, LL24 0AD

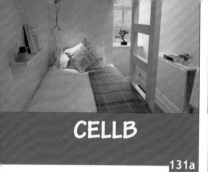

CELLB

131a

TREKS
BUNKHOUSE

131b

After a long day of adventures, why not rest your weary head in a former Edwardian police house, now a delightful self contained hostel?

Conveniently located in the centre of Blaenau Ffestiniog. This self contained unit is perfect for family or friends get togethers. It's an ideal location for adventures such as Zip World, Go Below, mountain and beach walks or mountain biking. CellB is the perfect place to recover, recuperate, and soak up the vibrant landscape.

Treks 4* Bunkhouse is in the mountains on the edge of the village of Blaenau Ffestiniog. Ideal for enjoying the rugged beauty of Snowdonia. It is a former golf club recently converted to provide self-catering accommodation for groups. Attractions nearby include Llechwedd Slate Caverns, Bounce Below, Zip World, Antur Stiniog, Ffestiniog & Welsh Highland Railways, Go Below Adventures, Coed y Brenin Mountain Bike Centre, Portmeirion Italian Village, White Water Rafting, Harlech Castle and Black Rock Sands.

      GROUPS ONLY

DETAILS

- **Open** - All year. All day
- **Beds** - 7:1x2,1x3 (bunk style beds),sofa bed sleeping 2
- **Price/night** - From £120. Min 2 nights.

CONTACT: Reception
Tel: 01766 832001
hostelcellb@outlook.com
cellb.org
Park Square, Blaenau Ffestiniog
LL41 3AD

 GROUPS ONLY

DETAILS

- **Open** - All year. Check in 3pm-8pm.
- **Beds** - 13
- **Price/night** - Sole use: £312. Min 2 night stay.

CONTACT: Dyfed
Tel: 07796 172318
treksbunkhouse@gmail.com
www.treksbunkhouse.co.uk
Y Cefn, Ffestiniog, Gwynedd, LL41 4PS

MAENTWROG
BUNKHOUSE
132a

SNOWDON LODGE
GROUP HOSTEL
132b

Maentwrog bunkhouse is a newly converted cowshed on a working farm. It has a fully equipped kitchen, underfloor heating, TV/DVD, BBQ area, laundry facilities, power washer and bike lockup. Local activities include hill walking (Moelwyn and Cnicht 10 mins away), white water rafting, Coed y Brenin cycling centre, Blaenau Ffestiniog down hill cycle track, RopeWorks & canyoning. Ffestiniog railway and beautiful beaches are within 15-20 mins' drive. The Welsh Coastal Path passes the end of the lane.

Snowdon Lodge, the birthplace of Lawrence of Arabia, is perfect for a get-together with friends & family. An ideal self-catering group base in Snowdonia. Large Victorian property set in 4-acre grounds in a pretty village. Sole use for your group. Pet friendly. Well-equipped kitchen. Spacious dining room. Cosy lounge. BBQ area. Private parking. Games room. Additional lecture/seminar/prayer room available for hire. En-suite bedrooms

DETAILS

- **Open** - All year.
- **Beds** - 4
- **Price/night** - £23pp. Bring sleeping bags or hire bed linen @£5/person/stay

DETAILS

- **Open** - January - December. All day.
- **Beds** - 35: doubles, twins and dorms.
- **Price/night** - Sole use starting from £750. Min of 2 nights, 3 on bank holidays.

CONTACT: Mrs Eurliw M Jones
Tel: 01766 590231
emj2@hotmail.co.uk
www.bunkhousesnowdonia.com
Felen Rhyd Fach, Maentwrog, Blaenau
Ffestiniog, Gwynedd, LL41 4HY

CONTACT: Carl or Anja
Tel: 01766 515354
info@snowdonlodge.co.uk
www.snowdonlodge.co.uk
Lawrence House, Church Street,
Tremadog, Nr Porthmadog, Gwynedd,
Snowdonia, LL49 9PS

BRYNKIR
COACH HOUSE
133a

ABERSOCH
SGUBOR UNNOS
133b

Formerly Cwm Pennant Hostel, Brynkir Coach House offers welcoming & relaxed accommodation for groups of 6-66 across dorms, en suite family/ private rooms & a 6-bed self-contained flat. Set within stunning grounds in the Snowdonia National Park with fantastic views of the Cwm Pennant valley & Moel Hebog. Local caterers are available. The area is ideal for hill walking, rock climbing, canoeing. For cyclists Lon Las Cymru is on the door step!

Bunkhouse accommodation on a family farm in the village of Llangian. Just one mile from Abersoch which is famed for watersports, the bunkhouse is an ideal base for walking the Llyn Coast Path, surfing, cycling, golf, fishing, running & sailing. Spinning & knitting courses using the farm's own wool are available. The three modern bunkrooms are ideal for individuals or groups with a fully equipped kitchen/lounge, disabled facilities, secure storage & parking.

DETAILS

- **Open** - All year
- **Beds** - 66: 1x15, 1x14, 1x9, 1x8, 1x6/8 (family en-suite), 2x2/3 (family ensuite). Flat for 6.
- **Price/night** - From £25pp, under 2's free. Min of 6 people.

DETAILS

- **Open** - All year. All day.
- **Beds** - 14: 2x4, 1x6
- **Price/night** - £22 (adult & children over 10), £10 children (10 years old & younger).

CONTACT: Dawn Harding
Tel: 01766 549321 or 07866 631538
dawnharding14@icloud.com
Golan, Garndolbenmaen, Gwynedd, LL51 9AQ

CONTACT: Phil or Meinir
Tel: 01758 713527
enquiries@tanrallt.com
www.tanrallt.com
Fferm Tanrallt Farm, Llangian, Abersoch, Gwynedd, LL53 7LN

LLANDUDNO
HOSTEL
134a

CONWY VALLEY
BACKPACKERS BARN
134b

Llandudno Hostel is a Victorian 4* boutique, award-winning hostel where individuals, families & groups (including schools) are welcome all year. Set in the heart of the Victorian seaside town of Llandudno, it's your perfect base for shopping & exploring many local attractions, including blue flag beaches, dry slope skiing, Zip World, Surf Snowdonia, bronze age copper mine, traditional pier, museums & fishing trips.

Conwy Valley Backpackers is situated on a peaceful organic farm in the heart of the beautiful Conwy Valley, with excellent access to Snowdonia. Centrally heated with a fully equipped self-catering kitchen, log fires and hot showers. Bike/canoe storage and tourist information are available.

Local activities include fishing, hiking, white water rafting and mountain biking. Surf Snowdonia is within walking distance and Zip World is a short drive.

DETAILS

- **Open** - All year (telephone in winter prior to arrival). All day.
- **Beds** - 46: 2x8,2x6,4x2,1x4,1xfamily(6)
- **Price/night** - From £20 per person, £55 per private twin room, £60 per private twin en suite. Group and family rates on request. Special offers autumn/winter.

CONTACT: James or Melissa
Tel: 01492 877430
info@llandudnohostel.co.uk
www.llandudnohostel.co.uk
14 Charlton Street, Llandudno, LL30 2AA

DETAILS

- **Open** - April to October
- **Beds** - 14: 1x4, 2x5
- **Price/night** - From £25pp. Sole use from £350.

CONTACT: Claudia
Tel: 01492 660504 or 07956 851425
info@conwyvalleybarn.com
www.conwyvalleybarn.com
Pyllau Gloewon Farm, Tal-y-Bont,
Conwy, Gwynedd, LL32 8YX

BRON-Y-GADER
BUNKHOUSE
135a

PLATTS FARM
BUNKHOUSE
135b

Perched at 290m (950ft) in the foothills of Snowdonia with direct access to the Carneddau mountains, Bron-y-Gader Bunkhouse offers comfortable & great value accommodation for up to 37.

Remote and isolated but just 8 miles to Conwy and 2 miles to the nearest pub.

The many attractions and high adrenaline activities in Snowdonia are just a short drive away.

Platt's Farm Campsite and 3* Bunkhouse is situated in a range of Victorian farm buildings, in the charming village of Llanfairfechan. Close to the A55, the Bunkhouse lies at the start/end of the 14 Welsh 3000 Peaks walks in the Snowdonia National Park, within a 10 min walk of the Wales Coastal Path and on the NCN 5 Cycle Route. Shops, pubs and cafés are within 5 mins' walk. Just 15 mins from Zipworld, Bethesda & 20 mins from Surf Snowdonia.

       **GROUPS ONLY**

DETAILS
- **Open** - March-Nov. Dec-Feb: see website
- **Beds** - 37: 4x8, 1x3, 1x2
- **Price/night** - £15pp. Minimum charge of 12 people, min stay of 2 nights. DofE, school & youth orgs: £11pp.

CONTACT:
info@bron-y-gader.org
www.bron-y-gader.org
Bron-y-Gader Centre, Llanbedr-y-Cennin, Conwy, LL32 8UT

DETAILS
- **Open** - All year. Check out before 11am, check in after 2pm.
- **Beds** - 10
- **Price/night** - £20pp. Sole use £180 per night.

CONTACT: Sam Davies
Tel: 01248 680105
sam@plattsfarm.com
www.plattsfarm.com
Platts Farm Bunkhouse, Aber Road,
Llanfairfechan, Conwy, LL33 0HL

CABAN CYSGU
GERLAN BUNKHOUSE
136a

Caban Cysgu, run by the community of Gerlan, offers purpose-built accommodation at the foot of the Carneddau. Perfect for walking in Snowdonia, it's a great base for the 'Fifteen 3000ft Peaks' long-distance challenge & The Slate Trail. Just 5 mins from Zip World; the longest and fastest zip line in Europe. There are also plenty of mountain bike trails on the doorstep while road cyclists have the Sustrans route 'Lôn Las Ogwen' just a mile away. For climbers, Idwal is close by, while Afon Ogwen is popular with canoeists.

DETAILS
- **Open** - All year. All day.
- **Beds** - 16 : 1x5, 1x2, 1x1, 1x8.
- **Price/night** - From £16 - £18

CONTACT: Dewi Emyln, Manager
Tel: 01248 605573 or 07464 676753
cabancysgu@hotmail.com
www.cabancysgu-gerlan.co.uk
Ffordd Gerlan, Gerlan, Bethesda,
Bangor, LL57 3ST

SNOWDONIA
MOUNTAIN HOSTEL
136b

In the heart of the Ogwen Valley and surrounded by the Welsh 3000s, this hostel is the perfect base for walkers, climbers and cyclists with the best routes straight from the door. Snowdon is a 30 minute drive away. For adventure seekers Zip World is within walking distance and the Anglesey beaches are a short drive. Newly refurbished, Snowdonia Mountain Hostel has comfy beds with linen & a superb kitchen diner. Sorry no stag or hen parties.

DETAILS
- **Open** - All year (sole use Nov- Mar)
- **Beds** - 24: 2x6, 2x4, 1x4 (self contained flat)
- **Price/night** - Check website

CONTACT: Neil Martinson
Tel: 01248 600416
info@snowdoniamountainhostel.com
www.snowdoniamountainhostel.com
Snowdonia Mountain Hostel, Tai Newyddion, Nant Ffrancon, Bangor LL57 3DQ

OGWEN VALLEY
BUNKHOUSE
137a

LODGE DINORWIG
137b

In Snowdonia National Park, just over a mile from the small town of Bethesda, Ogwen Valley Bunkhouse provides spacious, eco friendly accommodation for individuals, couples, families and groups. The large open plan communal area has a well equipped kitchen, a large dining table and plenty of comfy chairs. With underfloor heating, comfortable beds and a drying room guests invariably return. On Snowdonia Slate Trail & Lon Las Cymru .

On the edge of Snowdonia National Park, Lodge Dinorwig, a former school, has a 14 bed bunkroom. Breakfast is included and evening meals can be booked but there is no self-catering.

The main hall has a mixture of sofas, tables and chairs, ideal to relax and plan the next day. Perfectly located for all the high adrenaline activities Snowdonia has to offer and with easy access to attractions such as Zip World as well as Snowdon and Llanberis.

DETAILS
- **Open** - All year. Check out 10.30am.
- **Beds** - 16: 2x4, 1x6, 1x camp bed, 1x bed settee
- **Price/night** - £17pp. Please enquire for exclusive use prices.

DETAILS
- **Open** - Open all year around.
- **Beds** - 14: 1x14
- **Price/night** - £28-35pp. Sole use £340-420. Including breakfast.

CONTACT: Gwyn Morgan
Tel: 01248 601958 or 07775 978405
bookings@ogwenvalleybunkhouse.co.uk
www.ogwenvalleybunkhouse.co.uk
Capel Saron, Tyn Y Maes, Bethesda,
Gwynedd LL57 3LX

CONTACT: Sonni
Tel: 07593 818230
info@lodge-dinorwig.co.uk
www.lodge-dinorwig.co.uk/
Dinorwig, Caernarfon, Gwynedd,
LL55 3EY

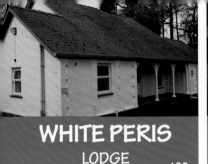

WHITE PERIS
LODGE
138a

White Peris Lodge is part of Blue Peris Mountain Centre in the heart of Snowdonia. The Lodge sleeps 13 across 4 rooms. Well equipped, there's a self catering kitchen, central heating, hot showers, bike storage, drying rooms, picnic tables & parking. While the Lodge is perfect for families & small groups, the main Centre sleeps 60 & is ideal for large groups & schools. Outdoor activities available.

DETAILS

■ **Open** - All year
■ **Beds** - Lodge 13: 1x6, 1x4, 1x2, 1x1. Mountain Centre: 60
■ **Price/night** - Adults £18pp. Under 18 £12. Under 1 FOC. 8+ adults £16. 10% discounts for 2+ nights. Bedding £2pppn.

CONTACT: Reception
Tel: 01286 870 853
Mark.Richards@fusion-lifestyle.com
www.blueperis.co.ukBlue Peris Mountain Centre, Dinorwic, Caernarfon, Gwynedd. LL55 3ET

OLD SCHOOL
LODGE
138b

In the small mountain village of Deiniolen, in the heart of Snowdonia, not far from Llanberis, The Old School Lodge is the perfect base for groups of all kinds wishing to explore the rugged splendour of North Wales. Perfect for groups of walkers or climbers, the Lodge provides high quality accommodation for those looking for a warm comfortable base to return to after a day on the Welsh mountains. Facilities include a well equipped self-catering kitchen, lounge, games room & resources room.

DETAILS

■ **Open** - All year. All day.
■ **Beds** - 38: 1x6, 7x4, 2x2
■ **Price/night** - £19.50pp. Scouts and Guides: £14.25. Minimum stay 2 nights, minimum charge based on 12 people.

CONTACT: Booking Secretary
Tel: 01516 324943
activities@oldschoollodge.org.uk
www.oldschoollodge.org.uk
Deiniolen, Caernarfon LL55 3HH

LON DRYLL
OUTDOORS
139a

PENTRE BACH
BUNKHOUSE
139b

Ideally situated on the edge of Snowdonia National Park yet just a 15 minute drive to the seaside town of Caernarfon, Lon Dryll is your perfect base for exploring North Wales. Under new ownership & completely refurbished, Lon Dryll offers groups of between 10-29 exclusive use of all its facilities. Guests will enjoy privacy, space & breath-taking panoramic views. Dogs are welcome.

Situated between Waunfawr and Betws Garmon, Pentre Bach Bunkhouse provides alpine style, dog friendly accommodation and a campsite.

The ground floor of the bunkhouse has a dining/cooking area while upstairs there are alpine sleeping platforms with mattresses for 16. Showers, toilets and washing/drying facilities, shared with the campsite, are just across the yard.

DETAILS

■ **Open** - All year. Check in from 5pm. Check out by 11am
■ **Beds** - 29: Bunkhouse 17: 1x6, 1x5, 1x4, 1x2. Main House 12: 2x5 1x2
■ **Price/night** - From £200. Peak season £350 for 12 in the main house plus £20pp for extra guests. Reduced rates for small groups, schools & long stays. 2 nights min.

CONTACT: Eve Williamson
Tel: 07921610696
info@londrylloutdoors.com
www.londrylloutdoors.com
Strata House, Dryll, LL55 3NF

DETAILS

■ **Open** - All year. All day. Enquires 9am - 9pm. Arrive from 4pm, leave by 11am.
■ **Beds** - 16: 1x16.
■ **Price/night** - £16pp (inc gas, electric & showers). Sole use bookings negotiable according to group size.

CONTACT: Karen Neil
Tel: 07798 733939 (9am-9pm)
info@pentrebachbunkhouse.co.uk
www.pentrebachbunkhouse.co.uk
Pentre Bach, Waunfawr, Caernarfon, Gwynedd, LL54 7AJ

RHYD DDU
OUTDOOR CENTRE
140a

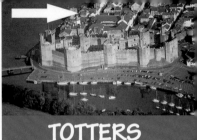

TOTTERS
140b

The Rhyd Ddu Bunkhouse provides group accommodation at the foot of Snowdon and the Nantlle Ridge. Sleeping 30 in 6 bedrooms, it has a fully equipped kitchen and a large communal dining room with a big screen. Glorious views, central heating, fast WiFi, parking, secure bike storage, drying room and garden. Bring your own sleeping bag, pillow case & towel. Pub, café, & steam train station all within 2 minutes' walk

Totters sits in the heart of the historic castle town of Caernarfon just 30m from the Menai Straits. Close to many pubs and restaurants but with good public transport to the Snowdonia National Park. The hostel is a 200 year old, five floored town house with five bedrooms sleeping either 4 or 6 and a huge double/family en suite. Opposite there is a self-catering town house sleeping 6.

       GROUPS ONLY

DETAILS

■ **Open** - All year. All day. Check in from 4pm, check out by 11am.
■ **Beds** - 30: 1x12, 4x4, 1x2
■ **Price/night** - Exclusive hire from £400. Great weekend group rates. 4 nights for the price of 3 on off-peak midweek dates.

DETAILS

■ **Open** - All year. All day. Check in by 10 pm.
■ **Beds** - 28: 3x6, 2x4, 1x2 (en suite), 1x2 (twin)
■ **Price/night** - £19.50pp in a dorm. £55 for a double/twin en suite. £47.50 for a twin. Discounts for groups.

CONTACT: Rob
Tel: 01286 882688
stay@canolfan-rhyd-ddu.cymru
www.snowdonia-bunkhouse.wales
The Old School, Rhyd Ddu, Snowdonia, Wales LL54 6TL

CONTACT: Bob/Henryette
Tel: 01286 672963 or 07979 830470
totters.hostel@gmail.com
www.totters.co.uk
Plas Porth Yr Aur, 2 High Street, Caernarfon, Gwynedd, LL55 1RN

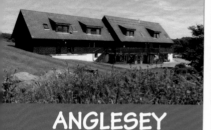

ANGLESEY
OUTDOOR CENTRE
141a

Anglesey Outdoors is an ideal base for groups, individuals or families. Just a mile from Porthdafarch Beach & the coastal path & only 2km from Sustrans Cycle Route 8. It has 4 self-contained areas each with their own self-catering & bathroom facilities. These can be hired individually or together. Optional full catering. There's an on-site bar/bistro & a drying room. Glamping also available.

DETAILS
- **Open** - All year. 24 hour access.
- **Beds** - 68: Main Centre 33: 1x7,4x5,1x4,1x2. Maris Annexe 10: 5x2. Ty Pen Annexe 8: 1x4,2x2. Gogarth Dorms 16: 1x7,1x7,1x2.
- **Price/night** - From £14pp (dorms) to £45pp (ensuite twin). Ask for sole use.

CONTACT: Penny Hurndall
Tel: 01407 769351
penny@angleseyoutdoors.com
www.angleseyoutdoors.com
Porthdafarch Road, Holyhead, Anglesey, LL65 2LP

OUTDOOR
ALTERNATIVE
141b

A family run 4* bunkhouse tucked away in Rhoscolyn, an AONB on the Anglesey Coast. Just 5 mins' walk to the sandy beach at Borthwen & a stone's throw from the Anglesey Coastal Path. Perfect for friends & families, outdoor groups, schools and universities. Your ideal base for kayaking, climbing, sailing, walking, bird watching or beach holidays. Eco conscious business. Nearby Holyhead has ferry links to Ireland.

DETAILS
- **Open** - All year. 24 hour access
- **Beds** - 41: 19:(1x2, 2x4, 1x5) + 22:(1x4, 4x4/5)
- **Price/night** - From £30pp. £966 for the weekend per bunkhouse. Discount for youth/school/uni groups and for 7-nights.

CONTACT: Jacqui Short
Tel: 01407 860469
enquiries@outdooralternative.co.uk
www.outdooralternative.co.uk
Cerrig-yr-Adar, Rhoscolyn, Holyhead, Anglesey, LL65 2NQ

South Scotland

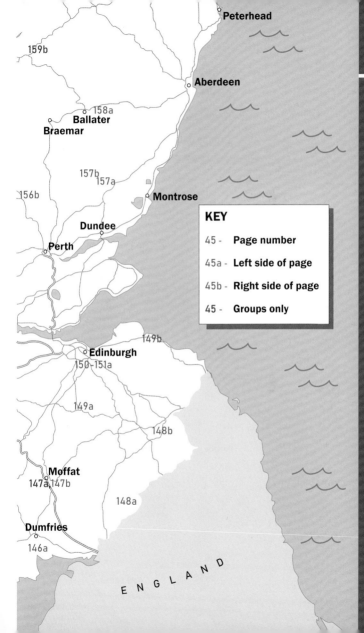

South Scotland

Peterhead

159b

Aberdeen

158a
Ballater
Braemar

157b
157a

156b

Montrose

Dundee

Perth

KEY

45 - **Page number**

45a - **Left side of page**

45b - **Right side of page**

45 - **Groups only**

149b

Edinburgh
150-151a

149a

148b

Moffat
147a 147b

148a

Dumfries

146a

E N G L A N D

North Scotland

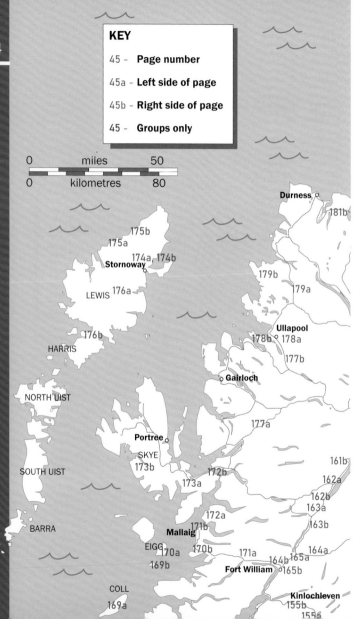

KEY

45 - **Page number**

45a - **Left side of page**

45b - **Right side of page**

45 - **Groups only**

| 0 | | miles | | 50 |
0 kilometres 80

Durness

181b

175b
175a
174a 174b
Stornoway

179b
179a

LEWIS 176a

Ullapool
178b 178a
177b

176b

HARRIS

Gairloch

NORTH UIST

177a

Portree
SKYE
173b
172b
173a

161b
162a
162b
163a
163b

SOUTH UIST

172a
171b
164a
Mallaig
BARRA
EIGG 170a 170b
171a 164b 165a
169b
Fort William 165b

COLL
169a

Kinlochleven
155b
155a

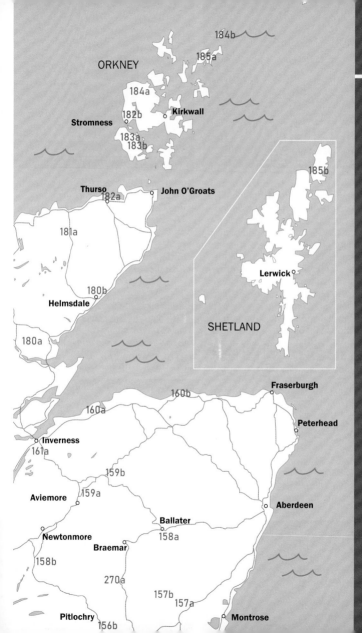

ORKNEY

184b

185a

184a

182b • Kirkwall

Stromness

183a
183b

Thurso 185b
182a • John O'Groats

181a

Lerwick •

180b

Helmsdale

SHETLAND

180a

Fraserburgh

160b

160a

Peterhead

• **Inverness**

161a

159b

159a

Aviemore

• **Newtonmore**

Ballater

158a

• **Aberdeen**

Braemar

158b

270a

157b
157a

Pitlochry 156b

• **Montrose**

North Scotland

MARTHROWN
OF MABIE
146a

Marthrown is set in the heart of Mabie Forest, 6 miles south of Dumfries. It has a sauna, a wood burning spring water hot tub, a large BBQ, garden areas, a challenge course and plenty of room for groups. There are a variety of mountain bike routes including the 7Stanes mountain bike trails nearby. Catered meals available for groups. As well as the bunkhouse, there are also Mongolian yurts, an American style tipi and the jewel in the crown is the Iron Age Roundhouse for parties or weddings.

DETAILS
- **Open** - All year. 10am-8pm - late arrival by arrangement.
- **Beds** - 18: 1x6, 1x4, 1x8 + Roundhouse, 4 Yurts, Tipi + Camping.
- **Price/night** - Please enquire

CONTACT: Mike or Pam Hazlehurst
Tel: 01387 247900 or 07786 628456
info@marthrownofmabie.co.uk
www.marthrownofmabie.co.uk
Mabie Forest, Dumfries, DG2 8HB

BARHOLM
ACCOMMODATION
146b

Barholm Enterprise Centre houses a variety of businesses including an Arts and Crafts Co-operative and Barholm Accommodation which has en suite shared and private rooms.

Perfect for cyclists, walkers, fishermen or those who generally enjoy the outdoors.

Facilities include a communal kitchenette (fridge/freezer, kettle, toaster and microwave), sitting room, on-site bike repair facilities & electric car charging.

DETAILS
- **Open** - All year. All day
- **Beds** - 28
- **Price/night** - From £20

CONTACT: Jenny Adams
Tel: 01671 820810
jenny.barholm@gmail.com
barholm-centre.co.uk
St Johns Street, Creetown, Dumfries and Galloway, DG8 7JE

WELL ROAD
CENTRE
147a

The Well Road Centre sits in its own grounds in the charming town of Moffat. It is ideal for all types of groups, family get togethers, conferences, residential workshops, sports and outdoor activity clubs. The Centre has two spacious meeting rooms, a large bright self-catering kitchen, dining room fully equipped for 65, games hall for indoor activities and table tennis room. Bring your own sleeping bags or linens for single duvets. Ample parking & storage.

 GROUPS ONLY

DETAILS
- **Open** - All year. All day.
- **Beds** - 70: in 13 rooms (2 en suite).
- **Price/night** - From £1400 for two night weekend for up to 50 people, plus £25 pp for each extra person. Linen packs for single beds £7.50 (booked in advance).

CONTACT: Ben Larmour
Tel: 01683 221040
ben8363@aol.com
www.wellroadcentre.com
Well Rd, Moffat, DG109BT

MOFFAT
INDEPENDENT HOSTEL
147b

This friendly family run hostel has been designed with comfort and the outdoor enthusiast in mind. Situated on the edge of the pretty town of Moffat, the hostel sleeps up to 20 in a selection of en-suite quad, twin & double rooms. It has bike/kayak storage, bike wash area, drying room and all bedding provided. A perfect stopover on the Lejog cycle route & the Southern Upland Way. Book a bed, a room or the whole place.

DETAILS
- **Open** - All year: Check in after 4pm. Check out by 10.30am. 24-hr access.
- **Beds** - 20: 1x4/5, 2x4, 3xtwin, 1xdbl.
- **Price/night** - Dorm £25pp. Twin from £55. Supieror double £75. Quad from £95. Sole use from £450 (low season).

CONTACT: Tom Wellings
Tel: 07920 460105
booking@moffathostel.com
moffathostel.com
Bridge House, Well Road, Moffat,
Dumfries and Galloway, DG10 9JT

NEWCASTLETON
BUNKHOUSE
148a

Opened in 2022, this community-run bunkhouse in the Scottish Borders sleeps up to 14 in 3 en suite rooms. Book by the room, or book sole use. With the Newcastleton 7stanes Mountain Biking Centre, the Reivers cycle route and the Cross Border Trail on the doorstep, it is very popular with cyclists and walkers. In a village location with eateries close by.

DETAILS
- **Open** - All year. Check in 4pm. Check out 10am
- **Beds** - 14: 2x4, 1x6 (all en suite)
- **Price/night** - From £100 for 4 bed room, £150 for 6 bed room. Discounts for multiple night stays.

CONTACT: Pauline Elliot
Tel: 01387 375908 (office hours)
info@newcastletonbunkhouse.com
newcastletonbunkhouse.com
Buccleuch House, 4 South Hermitage Street, Newcastleton, Scottish Borders. TD9 0QR

KIRK YETHOLM
FRIENDS OF NATURE
148b

Kirk Yetholm Friends of Nature House is perfectly located at the start/end of the Pennine Way. It is also close to St. Cuthbert's Way, the Borderloop Cycle Route and Sustrans Route 84. It's a great base too for local day hikes, ideal for individuals, families and small groups. Recently upgraded, the house offers a comfortable, friendly and peaceful retreat. Evening meals and breakfast are available in the adjacent hotel.

DETAILS
- **Open** - All year (Nov-Feb groups only). Check-in 5pm-10.30pm. Check-out 10am.
- **Beds** - 22: 1x7, 1x5, 1x4, 2x2 (twin), 1x2 (bunk).
- **Price/night** - From £24, under 18's from £20. Discounts for NFI / SYHA / HI

CONTACT: The Manager
Tel: 01573 420639
kirkyetholm@friendsofnature.org.uk
www.friendsofnature.org.uk
Friends of Nature House, Waukford, Kirk Yetholm, Kelso, Roxburghshire, TD5 8PG

CLEIKUM MILL
LODGE
149a

Cleikum Mill Lodge, in the heart of the Tweed Valley, sleeps 12; 8 in the Lower Mill & 4 in the Upper Mill. Book a room, a floor or the whole Mill. Innerleithen, a 7Stanes trail centre, is on the NCR1 & Southern Upland Way. Shops, pubs, cafés etc are a short stroll away. Dog friendly with sole use. Breakfast available at hotel opposite (by pre arrangement.)

DETAILS
- **Open** - All year. All day. Check in after 4pm, check out before 10am.
- **Beds** - 12: Lower:1x2,2x3. Upper: 2x2
- **Price/night** - £56 private single, £80 twin, £100 triple. Apartment for 4 £149. Apartment for 8 £296. Discounts from 12%-35% for 3+ nights, (the longer you stay the greater the discount.)

CONTACT: Graham
Tel: 07790 592747
hello@cleikum-mill-lodge.co.uk
www.cleikum-mill-lodge.co.uk
7 Cleikum Mill, High St, Innerleithen,
Scottish Borders EH44 6QT

DOLPHIN DUNBAR
@THE DOLPHIN INN
149b

The Dolphin Inn is situated in the centre of the historic seaside town of Dunbar. Just a short walk to the beach and the High Street and with the possibility of trying out a whole range of outdoor activities close by, the hostel is perfect for weekend breaks and family holidays. Having just been lovingly restored, this characterful hostel sleeps 27 across 11 rooms. Dogs are welcome by arrangement.

DETAILS
- **Open** - All year
- **Beds** - 27: 1x6, 1x3, 2xdbl (en suite) 4xdbl, 3xtwin
- **Price/night** - £30 for adults, £20 for children (12 and under), £25 for dorm beds.

CONTACT: Tom Page
Tel: 01368 868427 or 01414 270770
info@dolphindunbar.com
dolphindunbar.com
The Dolphin Inn, 2 Queens Road,
Dunbar, East Lothian EH42 1JZ

ROYAL MILE
BACKPACKERS
150a

CASTLE ROCK
HOSTEL
150b

Royal Mile Backpackers is a small and cosy hostel with its own special character! Perfectly located on the Royal Mile, the most famous street in Edinburgh, Royal Mile Backpackers is the ideal place to stay for the independent traveller.

The comfortable beds and cosy common areas will make you feel at home and the friendly staff are always on hand to help you make the most of your time in Edinburgh.

In a wonderful location, facing south with a sunny aspect and panoramic views over the city, Castle Rock Hostel is just steps away from the city centre. The historic Royal Mile, the busy pubs, the late-late nightlife of Grassmarket and Cowgate are all only a short walk away. Then, of course, there is the famous Edinburgh Castle.

Most of the rooms have no traffic noise and there are loads of great facilities, 24-hour reception and no curfew.

DETAILS

- **Open** - All year. Reception 6.30am - 3am (24 hrs during August).
- **Beds** - 46
- **Price/night** - From £10 per person. ID required for check in.

CONTACT: Receptionist
Tel: 0131 557 6120
royalmile@scotlandstophostels.com
www.royalmilebackpackers.com
105 High Street, Edinburgh, EH1 1SG

DETAILS

- **Open** - All year. Reception 24 hours.
- **Beds** - 302
- **Price/night** - From £14 per person. ID required for check in.

CONTACT: Receptionist
Tel: 0131 225 9666
castlerock@macbackpackers.com
www.castlerockedinburgh.com
15 Johnston Terrace, Edinburgh, EH1 2PW

HIGH STREET
HOSTEL
151a

EURO HOSTEL
GLASGOW
151b

The High Street Hostel is one of Europe's best regarded and most atmospheric hostels. It is hugely popular with world travellers. Located just off the historic Royal Mile in a 470 year old building, it is your perfect base for exploring all the city's many attractions and of course its wonderful nightlife.

Providing excellence in location, ambience and facilities, the hostel is highly recommended by more than ten of the world's top backpacker travel guides. Come along and see for yourself!

Glasgow city centre budget accommodation in a mix of private rooms, dorms and VIP suites for groups of 1-20. All rooms are en-suite with mobile cable charging stations. Free superfast WiFi. Perfect for shopping, sports events, gigs & exhibitions. Ideal for individuals & groups. Enjoy 'All You Can Eat' buffet breakfasts (£6.50pp), meal deals and drink promos in the bar. Just 5 mins from Central Station.

DETAILS

DETAILS

■ **Open** - All year. All day.
■ **Beds** - 156.
■ **Price/night** - From £14 per person. ID required for check in.

■ **Open** - All year. 24 hr reception. Check in from 3pm.
■ **Beds** - 452: in en suite private rooms, dorms, and VIP suites for groups.
■ **Price/night** - Beds from £10. Rooms from £20. VIP suites from £14pp. Book direct for Best Price Guarantee.

CONTACT: Reception
Tel: 0131 557 3984
highstreethostel@macbackpackers.com
www.highstreethostel.com
8 Blackfriars St., Edinburgh, EH1 1NE

CONTACT: The Reservations Team
Tel: 0845 539 9956
glasgow@eurohostels.co.uk
www.eurohostels.co.uk/glasgow
318 Clyde Street, Glasgow, G1 4NR

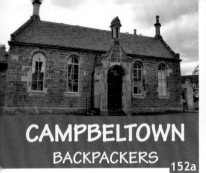

CAMPBELTOWN
BACKPACKERS
152a

152b

ARGYLL
BACKPACKERS

The Campbeltown Backpackers is housed in the Old Schoolhouse, a Grade B listed building.

The hostel offers easy access to the facilities of Campbeltown including swimming pool, gym, cinema and distillery tours. It is a good stop along the Kintyre Way which gives walkers spectacular views of the surrounding islands. The area also enjoys very good windsurfing, surfing, mountain bike routes and other major cycle trails.

DETAILS

- **Open** - All year. Leave by 10.30am on day of departure.
- **Beds** - 16: 1x6, 1x10
- **Price/night** - From £25 per person

CONTACT: Alan
Tel: 01586 551188
info@campbeltownbackpackers.co.uk
campbeltownbackpackers.co.uk
Kintyre Amenity Trust, Big Kiln, Campbeltown, Argyll, PA28 6JF

If you enjoy spectacular views and watching wildlife in modern comfortable self-catering accommodation then you'll love Argyll Backpackers! Located on the banks of Loch Fyne, just minutes from Cycle Route 78 in the hamlet of Inverneil, it's perfect for island hopping to Arran and Islay. Stock up on supplies from Tarbert or Ardrishaig / Lochgilphead.

DETAILS

- **Open** - All year (restrictions in winter).
- **Beds** - : 29: Hostel 24: 1x 2(dbl) ensuite, 1x 3(dbl+bunk) ensuite, 2x 2 ensuite, 2x 4 ensuite (5 if z-bed added),1x 6 ensuite. Flat: 5
- **Price/night** - From: dorm £35, double £65, single £50. Sole use £315-£550. Enquire for weddings & New Year.

CONTACT: Pam Richmond
Tel: 01546 603366 or 07786 157727
argyllbackpackers@sky.com
www.argyllbackpackers.com/
Loch Fyne Lodge, Inverneil, Ardrishaig, Argyll, PA30 8ES

TORRAN BAY
HOSTEL
153a

INVERARAY
HOSTEL
153b

With 16 en suite rooms, Torran Bay Hostel lies at the southern end of Loch Awe. A perfect base for your holiday.

Enjoy excellent fishing or launch your boat from Torran Farm land and spend the day on the 25 mile long loch. Other activities include hiking, cycling, bird watching or golf. Prices includes continental breakfast and all rooms have TV and DVD.

The historic town of Inveraray, on the western shore of Loch Fyne, is a superb location for exploring Scotland's Southern Highlands and Islands. Inverarary Hostel is perfect for independent holidaymakers who enjoy socialising.

The hostel offers simple, comfortable accommodation in private rooms, an excellent self-catering kitchen, communal dining area and a cosy wee lounge.

DETAILS

- **Open** - All year. All day.
- **Beds** - 34: 10x2 or double, 2 x double and single, 1x4 , 2x3
- **Price/night** - From £50 to £72 per room, including continental breakfast and parking. Group bookings welcome.

DETAILS

- **Open** - March 14th - late Oct. Reception 8-10am - 4-9pm.
- **Beds** - 22 in 10 rooms
- **Price/night** - Private rooms from £28pp.

CONTACT: Sheila Brolly
Tel: 01546 810133
sheilabro1@hotmail.co.uk
www.torranbayhostel.co.uk
Torran Farm, Ford, Lochgilphead. PA31 8RH

CONTACT: James
Tel: 01499 302562
info@inverarayhostel.co.uk
www.inverarayhostel.co.uk
Dalmally Road, Inveraray, Argyll, PA32 8XD

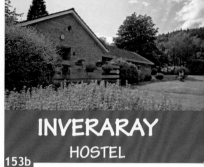

BALMAHA
BUNKHOUSE
154a

BY THE WAY
HOSTEL & CAMPSITE
154b

Reopening in 2023.

Set on the banks of Loch Lomond on the West Highland Way, Balmaha Bunkhouse offers quality assured accommodation for up to 13 at an affordable price. Bedding provided. Internet access via WiFi. The self-catering kitchen has cereal, milk, bread, tea and coffee for breakfast. The bunkhouse is ideal for walkers and outdoor enthusiasts, family get-togethers, corporate away-days, meetings, conferences or as a base to explore the wider area. Welcome to the romantic, adventurous and beautiful experience of Loch Lomond

By The Way Hostel & Campsite is in Loch Lomond National Park. There's excellent walking, climbing & white water rafting in the area. The accommodation includes camping, various huts, (hobbit houses, posh pods, glamping, trekker huts & camping cabins) & a purpose built 4* hostel with twin, double & dormitory rooms & great self-catering facilities. For more comfort still there are 2 chalets; one 3-bed, the other 2-bed.

DETAILS
- **Open** - Hostel/huts open from April-end Oct. Camping open from April to end Sept. 8am - 10am & 2pm - 8pm.
- **Beds** - 52: 26 hostel, 36 huts. Plus 50 camping & 2 chalets.
- **Price/night** - Dorms£25pp. Twin/double £50. Huts vary. Camping £12pp.

CONTACT: Kirsty Burnett
Tel: 01838 400333
info@tyndrumbytheway.com
www.TyndrumByTheWay.com
Lower Station Rd, Tyndrum, FK20 8RY

DETAILS
- **Open** - Arrive 2pm-7pm, leave by 10am
- **Beds** - 13 bunks; 1x6; 2x2; 1x2/3
- **Price/night** - From £30pp incl. b/fast

CONTACT:
ian@ariespensions.co.uk
Balmaha, Loch Lomond, G63 0JQ

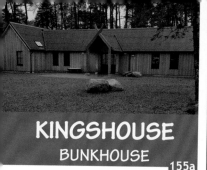

KINGSHOUSE
BUNKHOUSE
155a

HEART OF GLENCOE
HOLIDAYS
155b

Within the grounds of the famous Kingshouse Hotel, this brand new bunkhouse is right on the West Highland Way with spectacular Scottish mountain scenery. The Bunkhouse has 32 beds across 10 rooms. There is ample storage. Each each bunk has a locker, reading light, power socket, linen & towels. Ideal as a stop-over for travellers or a base to explore Glencoe & beyond.

There's skiing, walking & mountain biking on the doorstep. The Way Inn café offers all day dining & packed lunches. Open from 7.30am to 9pm daily (off-peak hours vary).

Heart of Glencoe Holidays, formerly known as Glencoe Independent Hostel lies in secluded woodland midway between Glencoe village and Clachaig Inn with access to world-class cycling, walking, climbing and kayaking. The Glencoe Ski Centre and The West Highland Way are just 20 mins away. The alpine bunkhouse sleeps up to 16 in 3 private rooms. There are two bothies, 4 luxury caravans and 3 luxury log cabins.

DETAILS
- **Open** - All year (phone in Nov and Dec). No reception, book in advance
- **Beds** - 75: hostel:26, bunkhouse:16, bothies: 1x5, 1x6, caravans: 4x4, cabins: 2x2, 1x3
- **Price/night** - From £13.50 to £50pp.

DETAILS
- **Open** - All year.
- **Beds** - 32: 1x6, 4x4, 5x2
- **Price/night** - From £35 per person.

CONTACT:
Tel: 01855 851259
contact@kingshousehotel.co.uk
www.kingshousehotel.co.uk/bunkhouse/
Glencoe, Argyll, PH49 4HY

CONTACT: Keith or Davina
Tel: 01855 811906
info@heartofglencoe.co.uk
www.heartofglencoe.co.uk
Heart of Glencoe Holidays, Glencoe, Highland, PH49 4HX

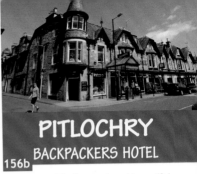

COMRIE
CROFT
156a

PITLOCHRY
BACKPACKERS HOTEL
156b

Comrie Croft is the Highland Edge retreat for hikers, families, friends & mountain bikers, just over an hour from Edinburgh & Glasgow. The eco-lodge offers beautiful en suite rooms with king-size beds, lots of wood & natural touches. Together with a barn, courtyard & wild places it is also available for sole use & weddings. On-site facilities include a field-to-fork café, bike shop & hire, lots of bike trails & farm shop. A footpath takes you to the village of Comrie & to stunning glens and mountains.

Located in the centre of beautiful Pitlochry, this friendly, cosy hostel is an old Victorian hotel literally bursting with character and provides dormitory and en suite private rooms. Comfy beds come with fitted sheets, duvets and 2 fluffy pillows and private rooms have fresh towels. The bright spacious lounge has comfy sofas and as many free hot drinks as you can drink. There's free WiFi, games, musical instruments and a free pool table. A great place to meet like minded people. You won't want to leave!

DETAILS

- **Open** - All year. All day.
- **Beds** - 48 + 14
- **Price/night** - Eco-lodge room: £40 per adult, £20 5-17 yrs. Under 5's Free

CONTACT: Someone Helpful
Tel: 01764 670140
info@comriecroft.com
www.comriecroft.com
Comrie Croft, By Crieff/Comrie,
Perthshire, PH7 4JZ

DETAILS

- **Open** - March to Nov. 9-11am & 5-10pm (times may vary).
- **Beds** - 79.
- **Price/night** - From £25pp for dorms. Private rooms from £30pp

CONTACT: Receptionist
Tel: 01796 470044
info@pitlochrybackpackershotel.com
pitlochrybackpackershotel.com
134 Atholl Road, Pitlochry, PH16 5AB

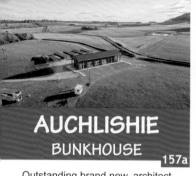

AUCHLISHIE
BUNKHOUSE
157a

Outstanding brand new, architect designed bunkhouse situated outside Kirriemuir, at the gateway to the Angus Glens. The bunkhouse offers excellent opportunities for outdoor enthusiasts to experience and enjoy the proximity to the Cairngorms National Park .

This eco bunkhouse, with solar panels and air source heat pumps, provides top quality accommodation for up to 24.

DETAILS
- **Open** - All year
- **Beds** - 24: 2x twin/double, 1x20
- **Price/night** - Dorm £30pp. Private rooms (as twin or double) £45pp, single occupancy £65. Dogs £10 per stay. Minimum stay 2 nights over weekends

CONTACT: Nicky Helyer
Tel: 07905 359648
events@auchlishie.co.uk
auchlishie.co.uk/bunkhouse.php
Auchlishie Farm, Kirriemuir, Angus
DD8 4LS

PROSEN
HOSTEL
157b

Glenprosen is the most intimate of the Angus Glens on the southernmost edge of the Cairngorms National Park. Two Munros; the Mayar and Driesh link Glenprosen to the Cairngorms plateau. Prosen Hostel is also close to the upgraded East Cairngorms footpath network. Converted to the latest and greenest specification, the 4* hostel offers cosy, quality accommodation for 18. With 4 rooms, sleeping 4, 4 and 6 in bunks and a family room sleeping 4. You can also hire the nearby village hall.

DETAILS
- **Open** - All year. All day.
- **Beds** - 18:1x6, 3x4
- **Price/night** - £25pp. Min periods & prices apply for Xmas and New Year.

CONTACT: Hector or Robert
Tel: 01575 540302
hectormaclean@compuserve.com
www.prosenhostel.co.uk
Prosen Hostel, Balnaboth, Kirriemuir,
Angus, DD8 4SA

BALLATER
HOSTEL
158a

DALWHINNIE
OLD SCHOOL HOSTEL
158b

Ballater Hostel lies in the centre of Ballater, near Balmoral, on the east side of the Cairngorms National Park. Traditional dorms & private rooms, along with a large open plan kitchen/dining/communal area make a great space to relax . Drying room and cycle storage available. Either book the whole hostel, a room or just a bed with no minimum stay. Excellent facilities, comfortable beds and a warm and friendly welcome awaits you - the kettle is always on!

Dalwhinnie Old School Hostel is in the former village primary school, set in an acre of ground. Directly opposite the train station, it's a perfect base to climb the many Munros in the area, as a stop over on the N7 cycle route, for mountain biking at nearby Laggan Wolftrax, or simply as a beautiful overnight stop when visiting Skye or the NC 500.

Situated in the Cairngorms National Park it is across the field from the famous Dalwhinnie Distillery.

DETAILS
- **Open** - All year. Reception 8-10am / 5-10pm.
- **Beds** - 29:1x8,1x6,1x4,1x2,3x3 (family)
- **Price/night** - Dorm beds £20.50. Private rooms from £34.50.

CONTACT: Dominique or Daniel
Tel: 01339 753752
info@ballater-hostel.com
www.ballater-hostel.com
Ballater Hostel, Bridge Square, Ballater, AB35 5QJ

DETAILS
- **Open** - All year
- **Beds** - 27: 1x10, 2x6, 1xdbl+sgl, 1xdbl.
- **Price/night** - From £20pp. Private rooms from £55 per room.

CONTACT: Lee Cleghorn
Tel: 07960 174462
dalwhinniehostel@gmail.com
dalwhinniehostel.weebly.com
Ben Alder Road, Dalwhinnie, Highland, PH19 1AB

FRAOCH
LODGE
159a

GLENBEG
BUNKHOUSE & BOTHY
159b

Run by outdoor fans who have hosted walkers, cyclists and families for over 20 years, Froach Lodge is more then just a place to stay. Andy and Rebecca will help you or your group organise a fantastic activity each day. The Lodge is a warm and welcoming. Accommodation is in private twin/triple rooms, there is log burner in the lounge and space for drying and storing outdoor gear. A self catering kitchen is available or you can treat yourself to Rebecca's delicious home cooking.

Glenbeg Bunkhouse & Bothy are part of the award-winning Cairngorms Activities Centre, situated just outside Grantown-on-Spey in the Cairngorms National Park. The well-equipped bunkhouse sleeps 27 in 3 bedrooms, while the cosy bothy sleeps 6 in one bunkroom. Outdoor activities are available. Aviemore, Speyside Way, Dava Way & the River Spey are all close by.

DETAILS
- **Open** - 24 hour access, all year round.
- **Beds** - 37: Bunkhouse 27. Bothy 6. Overflow cabin 4.
- **Price/night** - Glenbeg Bunkhouse: £450 (Apr-Sep). £300 (Nov-Mar) Glenbeg Bothy: £100 (Apr-Sep). £85 per night (Nov-Mar).

DETAILS
- **Open** - All year
- **Beds** - 12: 6 x 2 or 3
- **Price/night** - Rooms available from £45. Enquire for whole hostel rates.

CONTACT: Andy or Rebecca
Tel: 01479 831 331
info@scotmountainholidays.com
scotmountainholidays.com
Deshar Road, Boat of Garten, Inverness-shire, PH24 3BN

CONTACT: Cairngorms Activities
Tel: 01479 873283
info@cairngormsactivities.co.uk
www.cairngormsactivities.
co.ukGlenbeg, Grantown-on-Spey, Moray, PH26 3NT

FINDHORN
VILLAGE HOSTEL
160a

160b
THE SAIL LOFT
BUNKHOUSE

Findhorn Village Hostel is right by the beautiful Moray Coast. Great wildlife sites & the Speyside distilleries are within reach. It provides newly renovated self-catering accommodation for groups or individuals. It has shared bunkrooms, a two-person room & an en suite family room. A studio flat (6 beds) has a small kitchenette & en suite shower rooms.

Situated on the shore of the Moray Firth coast in Portsoy, The Sail Loft has a stunning location. Converted from a former sail making loft, The Sail Loft is modern and well equipped. It provides self-catering accommodation for 25 in a mixture of single accessible, twin, triple and bunk rooms, with secure cycle storage, cycle wash-down facilities and an outdoor wood fired hot tub. The Sail Loft is a short easy walk from Portsoy town centre and its charming 17th century historic harbour. Groups welcome.

DETAILS
- **Open** - All year. Office: 10am-3pm Mon-Fri.
- **Beds** - 33: 2x10, 1x4, 1x2/3, studio flat for 6.
- **Price/night** - £25pp, Mates Cabin £50, Captains Suite £100, Lobster Pot £130. Discounts for groups. Whole Hostel from £475.

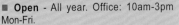

DETAILS
- **Open** - All year.
- **Beds** - 25: 1x6, 1x4, 2x3 (sgl), 4x2 (sgl), 1x1 (accessible)
- **Price/night** - From £25 per person.

CONTACT: Richard
Tel: 01309 692339 or 07496 230266
findhornvillagecentre@gmail.com
www.findhornvillagehostel.com
Church Place, Findhorn, Forres, Moray,
IV36 3YR

CONTACT: Ian Tillett
Tel: 01261 842222 or 01261 842695
contact@portsoysailloft.org
www.portsoysailloft.org/
Back Green, Portsoy, AB45 2AF

INVERNESS
STUDENT HOTEL
161a

LOCH NESS
BACKPACKERS LODGE
161b

The cosy and friendly Student Hotel enjoys panoramic views of the town and the mountains beyond. Your perfect place to unwind, just yards from the city's varied night-life and a few mins' walk from bus and train stations. Relax in the fabulous lounge with real log fire and drink as much free tea, coffee & hot chocolate as you like. Visit the beautiful ancient pine forest of Glen Affric or the Culloden Battlefield. Famous Loch Ness lies just a few miles upstream and of course has its own special wild animal.

This former Highland farmhouse provides warm & friendly hostel accommodation. Ideally situated within walking distance of Loch Ness, Urquhart Castle, the Great Glen Way & with pubs, restaurants & supermarket close by. Residents-only bar. Hiking tours, fishing, watersports, mountain biking can be arranged locally. Whisky & beer tasting by arrangement. Catering for groups of 10+. Pet-friendly by arrangement.

DETAILS

DETAILS

■ **Open** - April-Sept as a hostel. Oct-March as an exclusive use venue.
■ **Beds** - 43: 2x7, 2x6, 1x4, 1xtwin, 1xdouble, 2xfamily
■ **Price/night** - From £22pp. Discounts apply to groups.

■ **Open** - All year. All day. Reception 9-11am & 5-10pm
■ **Beds** - 57
■ **Price/night** - From £23.

CONTACT: Receptionist
Tel: 01463 236556
info@invernessstudenthotel.com
invernessstudenthotel.com/
6 - 8 Culduthel Road, Inverness
IV2 4AB

CONTACT: Patrick & Nikki Kipfmiller
Tel: 01456 450807
info@lochness-backpackers.com
www.lochness-backpackers.com
Coiltie Farmhouse, East Lewiston,
Drumnadrochit, Inverness, IV63 6UJ

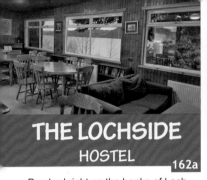

THE LOCHSIDE
HOSTEL
162a

162b

MORAGS LODGE
LOCH NESS

Perched right on the banks of Loch Ness, the Lochside Hostel has fantastic views up and down the loch and can give you direct access to the water's edge. Why not go for a dip in Scotland's largest water body? Take a walk to watch for wildlife? Or even hunt the elusive Nessie?

The Great Glen walking route passes the front door, and the End to End cycle route is nearby. Drumnadrochit is just 12 miles away by boat.

A multi-award winning 4* hostel with a range of rooms to meet all needs and budgets in the bustling village of Fort Augustus on the banks of Loch Ness. Your perfect base to explore the Loch Ness area and an ideal stop off on the Great Glen Way. Surrounded by stunning mountain scenery and set in wooded grounds the hostel boasts 24 hour self-catering facilities, excellent home-made meal options, a rustic bar, free WiFi, and ample car parking.

DETAILS

■ **Open** - April-October. Check in 17:00-23:00. Check out 10:30.
■ **Beds** - 47: 3x2 (twin), 2x4 (female), 5x4, 1x5, 1x8 all mixed dorms.
■ **Price/night** - From £15

DETAILS

■ **Open** - All year. Check in from 4pm (earlier by arrangement).
■ **Beds** - 75: 7x6, 6x4, 4x2/3
■ **Price/night** - From £27pp in dorm beds. Doubles/twins from £33pp. Family rooms from £86.

CONTACT: Reception
Tel: 01320 351274
lochside@macbackpackerstours.com
lochsidehostel.com
Alltsigh, Inverness. IV63 7YD

CONTACT: Claire
Tel: 01320 366289
info@moragslodge.com
www.moragslodge.com
Bunoich Brae, Fort Augustus, PH32 4DG

SADDLE MOUNTAIN
HOSTEL

163a

Saddle Mountain Hostel is a friendly 4* hostel in Invergarry, between Loch Ness & Fort William, at the junction with the road to Skye. Shortlisted for Hostel of the Year in The TGO Magazine Awards 2019 & 2020. The hostel sleeps 22 in 5 bedrooms (4 private & 1 dormitory), has a large kitchen, dining room, lounge, & drying room. Perfect for Munro bagging, long distance hiking, cycling, paddling & day trips.

DETAILS

- **Open** - Seasonal. Check website for availability. Check-in 4.30-10pm.
- **Beds** - 22: 1x6, 1x5 (1 double, 3 singles), 2x4, 1x3 (1 double, 1 single)
- **Price/night** - Dorm bed £27.50pp, private rooms from £21.50pp. Exclusive use price on request.

CONTACT: Helen or Gregor
Tel: 01809 501412
info@saddlemountainhostel.scot
www.saddlemountainhostel.scot
Mandally Road, Invergarry, PH35 4HP

GREAT GLEN
HOSTEL

163b

Located between mountains and lochs 20 miles north of Fort William and 10 miles south of Loch Ness, the Great Glen Hostel is your ideal base. Perfect for touring the Highlands, bagging Munros or paddling rivers and lochs. It's only a short walk to the Great Glen Way. The hostel provides comfortable, well appointed accommodation in twin, family and dormitory rooms and has a shop where you can buy your essentials.

DETAILS

- **Open** - All year. All day. Please call first Nov-March.
- **Beds** - 50: 2x2, 2x3, 4x5, 2x6, 1x8
- **Price/night** - Dorm beds from £23. Twin rooms from £26 pp. Whole hostel for sole use from £500 per night.

CONTACT: Vicky
Tel: 01809 501430
bookings@greatglenhostel.com
www.greatglenhostel.com
South Laggan, Spean Bridge,
Invernesshire, PH34 4EA

ÀITE
CRUINNICHIDH

164a

SMIDDY
BUNKHOUSE

164b

Àite Cruinnichidh, 15 miles northeast of Fort William, occupies a unique sheltered spot adjacent to the Monessie Gorge where you can explore remote glens, mountain passes and lochs.

The hostel has a fully equipped kitchen/dining room, sitting room, excellent showers, sauna & garden. All bedding is provided. Guests enjoy socialising and the natural environment setting.

Enjoy our loch-side location overlooking the Caledonian Canal, with Ben Nevis & Fort William 4 miles away. Ideal for the outdoor enthusiast with advice & guiding available for walking/climbing, river, loch and sea kayaking, open canoeing & dinghy sailing. Outdoor equipment hire available. After a busy day in the fresh air return to a welcome drying room & laundry, hot showers and a comfy private bunkroom ideal for families & groups.

DETAILS

- **Open** - All year
- **Beds** - 28: 1x6, 4x4, 1x twin, 1x double, 1x family/double en suite.
- **Price/night** - From: £22 (4 bed dorm), Twin £25pp. Double £27pp. Double en suite £30pp. Min of 4 people in winter.

CONTACT: Gavin or Nicola
Tel: 01397 712315
gavin@highland-hostel.co.uk
www.highland-hostel.co.uk
1 Achluachrach, By Roy Bridge, Near Fort William, PH31 4AW

DETAILS

- **Open** - All year. Check-in from 3pm - 8pm. Check-out 10am
- **Beds** - 24: 2x4,1x4 family,1x6,1x6 fam.
- **Price/night** - 4 bed room £92-£107. 4 bed en suite £101-£119. 6 bed room £137-£160. 6 bed en suite £147-£168.

CONTACT: Tina Cuthbertson
Tel: 01397 772467
enquiry@highland-mountain-guides.co.uk
www.accommodation-fortwilliam.co.uk
Snowgoose Mountain Centre, Station Road, Corpach, Fort William, PH33 7JH

CHASE THE WILD GOOSE
HOSTEL
165a

FORT WILLIAM
BACKPACKERS
165b

Chase The Wild Goose Hostel is on the Great Glen Way in the village of Banavie, near Fort William, at the end of the West Highland Way. You can be sure of a warm welcome, a comfortable bed and the company of like-minded travellers in a pleasant out-of-town environment. Whether you are on a relaxing holiday with family or friends, enjoying the adventure of a lifetime or travelling the world. Take time out in the Scottish Highlands. The scenery is breath-taking! The hospitality is second to none!

Surrounded by spectacular mountain scenery, Fort William is a mecca for those with a spirit of adventure. You can start (or end) the West Highland Way in Fort William, hike or bike along mountain trails, go for a boat trip on the sea loch or just take it easy amidst the wonderful scenery. Even in winter Fort William stays busy with skiing, snow-boarding, mountaineering and ice-climbing. Set on a hillside above the town, with wonderful views, this cosy hostel provides all you'll need after a day in the hills.

DETAILS
- **Open** - April-September
- **Beds** - 38 : 3x4, 1x5, 1x6, 1x7, 1x8
- **Price/night** - From £25 per person. Exclusive use is available to groups.

CONTACT: Daniel & Jo
Tel:
bookings@great-glen-hostel.com
www.chasethewildgoosehostel.co.uk
Great Glen Way, Banavie, Fort William, Inverness-shire, PH33 7LY

DETAILS
- **Open** - All year. Reception: 10am-12 noon & 5-10pm
- **Beds** - 42: 5x8, 1 x twin
- **Price/night** - From £25 per person. ID required for check-in.

CONTACT: Receptionist
Tel: 01397 700711
info@fortwilliambackpackers.com
fortwilliambackpackers.com
Alma Road, Fort William, PH33 6HB

OBAN
BACKPACKERS
166a

Perfectly situated in the heart of Oban, the gateway to the Isles, just 10 mins' walk from the bus, train & ferry terminals, this friendly hostel is a great place to stay and unwind. The fabulous sociable lounge has a real fire, pool table, free WiFi, comfy sofas and unlimited free hot drinks. The kitchen is fully equipped, perfect for cooking your favourite meals. Large dorm beds come complete with bedding including 2 comfy pillows. The hot powerful showers are legendary! Knowledgeable and friendly staff will help you make the most of your time in Oban.

DETAILS
- **Open** - March - Nov. 7-11am & 5-10 pm
- **Beds** - 54: 1x12, 1x10, 1x8, 4x6
- **Price/night** - From £23. Whole hostel bookings please email for quote.

CONTACT: Reception
Tel: 01631 562107
info@obanbackpackers.com
obanbackpackers.com/
Breadalbane Street, Oban, PA34 5NZ

CORRAN
HOUSE
166b

A warm welcome & great value accommodation in Oban for singles, couples, families & groups. Enjoy a large self-catering kitchen, spacious lounge, comfortable rooms & big beds. Corran House is perfect for exploring Argyll & the inner Hebrides & is close to the bus, train & ferry. Downstairs try Markie Dans bar for tasty meals, live music & Highland hospitality.

DETAILS
- **Open** - All year. Reception & check In: 3-10pm only.
- **Beds** - 26 bunks: 5x4, 1x6. Plus 26 private guest rooms
- **Price/night** - Bunks £18/£20 en suite. Guest rooms £27.50-£40pp (2 sharing). Singles from £45. Winter discounts.

CONTACT:
Tel: 01631 566040
enquiries@corranhouseoban.co.uk
www.corranhouseoban.co.uk
1-3 Victoria Cres, Corran Esplanade, Oban, Argyll, PA34 5PN

LISMORE
BUNKHOUSE

167a

This super warm and comfy eco bunkhouse on a traditional croft is the perfect base to explore the magical Isle of Lismore. The bunkhouse sleeps 12 in a mix of en suite dorms and private rooms and there is a campsite with 5 pitches and hook ups for 2 camper vans. The Isle of Lismore is just 7 miles by car ferry from Oban and is a tranquil, unspoilt island surrounded by stunning mountain scenery. Perfect for wildlife and history as well as walkers, cyclists and those wanting to get away from it all. Home grown organic veg and bike hire.

DETAILS

- **Open** - All year.
- **Beds** - 12
- **Price/night** - From £20pp. Exclusive hire available. Camping £10 pp.

CONTACT: Clare
Tel: 07720 975433
lismorebunkhouse@gmail.com
www.fb.com/thelismorebunkhouse/
Isle of Lismore, PA34 5UG

CRAIGNURE
BUNKHOUSE

167b

Craignure, a superior eco-sensitive bunkhouse, purpose built in 2014, is the perfect base for your Mull adventure. Set on the water's edge close to the ferry port, there's the Craignure Inn next door for traditional island hospitality.

The 4 well-appointed bunkrooms have en suite showers and there's a spacious well-appointed communal area with kitchen, ample dining and relaxing space.

DETAILS

- **Open** - All year. Closed 10am-4pm for cleaning.
- **Beds** - 20: 2x4, 2x6
- **Price/night** - Please call for rates or look on website.

CONTACT: Ivan or Claire
Tel: 01680 812043
info@craignure-bunkhouse.co.uk
www.craignure-bunkhouse.co.uk/
Craignure Bunkhouse, Craignure, Isle Of Mull, Argyll And Bute, PA65 6AY

ROSS OF MULL
BUNKROOMS
168a

COLONSAY
BACKPACKERS LODGE
168b

Ross of Mull Bunkrooms are located less than a mile from the ferry link to Iona at Fionnphort. Ideal for exploring the superb wildlife, rich history & shell-sand beaches of the Ross of Mull, so loved by outdoor enthusiasts.

Perfect for day trips to Staffa, the Treshnish Isles & Iona.

There are two 4 bed bunk rooms, a well-equipped kitchen, woodburner and stunning views.

Come to Colonsay Backpackers Lodge and savour the idyll of this Inner Hebridean island. Explore the magnificent sandy beaches, ancient forests and beautiful lochs.
Wildlife abounds; spot dolphins, seals, otters and many rare birds. The pub, café & shop are 3 miles away. Or buy fresh lobster, crab and oysters from the fishing boats. The lodge is a refurbished former gamekeeper's house with bothies. Centrally heated, it has 2 twin, 3 twin bunk and 2 three-bedded rooms. Free WiFi.

DETAILS
- **Open** - All year. Whole cottage only.
- **Beds** - 8: 2x4
- **Price/night** - Flexible rates from £50 - £160 depending on number of guests, time of year and length of stay.

CONTACT: Rachel Oliver
Tel: 07759 615200
info@rossofmullbunkrooms.co.uk
www.rossofmullbunkrooms.co.uk
Fionnphort, Isle of Mull PA66 6BL

DETAILS
- **Open** - April to October. 24 hours
- **Beds** - 16: 5x2, 2x3
- **Price/night** - £32pp twin, £27pp bothy

CONTACT: The Manager
Tel: 01951 200211
cottages@colonsayholidays.co.uk
www.colonsayholidays.co.uk
Colonsay Estate Cottages, Isle of Colonsay, Argyll, PA61 7YP

COLL
BUNKHOUSE
169a

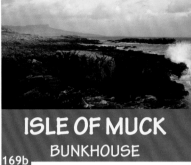

ISLE OF MUCK
BUNKHOUSE
169b

This 5* self-catering hostel accommodation is a short hop from the ferry terminal & in the village next to local amenities. Ideal for groups, families (cot available) or individuals. Short or longer stays. A half hour from the mainland by plane, under 3 hours by ferry. This beautiful Hebridean island is ideal for walking, stargazing, wildlife, cycling, water sports or chilling amidst stunning scenery. Visit quiet and beautiful spaces and beaches and enjoy fine island hospitality. A warm welcome awaits you.

This self-catering hostel can also be hired as a holiday cottage. The bunkhouse overlooks the ferry port of Port Mor, it is near to The Tearoom and to the island's Community Hall. The Isle of Muck is just 2 miles long by 1 mile wide and has a population of 35 people. With a rich cultural heritage and amazing wildlife, Muck is the perfect place to unwind. BYO bedding/towel or hire them from the hostel. Bring your own food supplies (no general store on Muck).

DETAILS

- **Open** - All year. 24 hours
- **Beds** - 14: 1x3(dbl), 1x5(dbl), 1x6
- **Price/night** - From £26pp with exclusive-use rooms and whole hostel hire rates available.

DETAILS

- **Open** - All year. Reasonable monthly lets available out of season.
- **Beds** - 8: 3x2(bunks) 1x2 (double)
- **Price/night** - £22pp (plus £5 per stay for bed linen and £3 for towels). £90/night exclusive use. £500/week exclusive use.

CONTACT:
Tel: 01879 230217
info@collbunkhouse.co.uk
www.collbunkhouse.com
Arinagour, Isle of Coll, Argyll, PA78 6SY

CONTACT: Ruth MacEwen
Tel: 01687 462362
info@isleofmuck.com
www.isleofmuck.com/
Port Mor, Isle of Muck, PH41 2RP

GLEBE BARN

170a

ARDNAMURCHAN
BUNKHOUSE

170b

Glebe Barn offers 4* homely accommodation on the extraordinary Isle of Eigg. It is situated within 1 mile of the island shop & café/restaurant. Offering outstanding sea views, it sleeps up to 22 in twin, triple, family & dorm rooms. Perfect for individuals, families or groups. Also two person mezzanine apartment.

Ardnamurchan Bunkhouse is in Glenborrodale on the Ardnamurchan Peninsula, one of the UK's last unspoiled coastal wildernesses.

This recently renovated eco-bunkhouse sleeps 16 people in eight bedrooms, with a well-equipped kitchen, flexible dining tables, free Wi-Fi and parking.

DETAILS

- **Open** - Groups all year; individuals from April to October. Open 24 hours.
- **Beds** - 22: 1x2, 2x3, 1x6, 1x8.
- **Price/night** - Dormitory bed: £22 (1-6 nights), £20 (7+ nights). Twin room £44 (1-6 nights), £40 (7+nights). Triple room £66 (1-7 nights), £60 (7+ nights). Contact for quote for groups.

CONTACT: Tamsin or Stuart
Tel: 0330 2210599 or 07951 785531
mccarthy@glebebarn.co.uk
www.glebebarn.co.uk
Glebe Barn, Isle of Eigg, Inner Hebrides, PH42 4RL

DETAILS

- **Open** - March to October
- **Beds** - 16: 2x1, 3x2, 2 doubles and 1xfamily (dbl +bunks)
- **Price/night** - From: Twin room £50. Double room £58. Family room £78. Single room £38. Contact for prices for groups and sole use throughout the year.

CONTACT: Fay and Niall Rowantree
Tel: 01972 500742 or 07749 727878
admin@theardnamurchanbunkhouse.co.uk
www.theardnamurchanbunkhouse.co.uk
Glenborrodale, Ardnamurchan, West Highlands, Scotland PH36 4JP

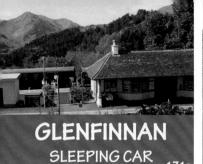

GLENFINNAN
SLEEPING CAR
171a

Glenfinnan Sleeping Car provides unique accommodation in an historic railway carriage next to Glenfinnan Station & close to Glenfinnan Viaduct (featured in Harry Potter films). An ideal location for the mountains, a good starting point for bothy expeditions & a useful stop-over en-route to Skye. Fully equipped kitchen, shower & drying room. Evening meals are available within walking distance

DETAILS
- **Open** - All year (enquire for winter opening details).
- **Beds** - 10
- **Price/night** - First night: £150 for up to 4 people plus £10pp thereafter. Additional nights: £100 for up to 4 people plus £10pp. Bedding/towel hire £5 per stay.

CONTACT: Amy or John
Tel: 01397 722295 or 07977 821480
glenfinnanstationmuseum@gmail.com
www.glenfinnanstationmuseum.co.uk
Glenfinnan Station, Glenfinnan, nr Fort William, PH37 4LT

SHEENAS
BACKPACKERS LODGE
171b

The Backpackers Lodge, the oldest croft house in Mallaig, offers a homely base from which to explore the Inner Hebrides, the famous white sands of Morar and the remote peninsula of Knoydart. Mallaig is a working fishing village with all the excitement of the boats landing. You can see the seals playing in the harbour and take whale and dolphin watching trips. The hostel provides excellent budget accommodation with central heating, a well equipped kitchen/common room and free WiFi. Hot water and heating provided by renewable energy.

DETAILS
- **Open** - All year. 9am-8pm
- **Beds** - 8: 2x4
- **Price/night** - From £25pp. Please phone for price and availability

CONTACT: Ashley or Fraser
Tel: 01687 462764
backpackers@btinternet.com
www.mallaigbackpackers.co.uk
Harbour View, Mallaig, PH41 4PU

KNOYDART
BUNKHOUSE
172a

SKYE
BACKPACKERS
172b

Welcome to the world famous Knoydart Foundation Bunkhouse on the stunning remote peninsula of Knoydart on the west coast of Scotland reachable only by boat or a long hike. Community run, the Bunkhouse uses hydro electricity & promotes responsible tourism. Set amid wild, remote terrain overlooking a mesmerising beach. Ten mins' walk to pub, PO, shop & ferry at Inverie. 3 bedrooms & comfy communal areas. Ranger service & deer stalking available. Stunning dark skies, so bring a torch!

Whether your visit to Skye is to tackle the mighty mountains, meet the legendary faeries or simply to chill out, Skye Backpackers is the place for you. Located in the fishing village of Kyleakin surrounded by mountains and sea, the hostel has dorm, double and twin rooms. All beds come with sheets, duvets and 2 pillows. There is a fully equipped self-catering kitchen, a sunny dining area, as much free tea, coffee & hot chocolate as you can drink, free WiFi, a cosy lounge with a real fire and spectacular views.

DETAILS
- **Open** - All year.
- **Beds** - 26: 1x7, 1x8, 1x11
- **Price/night** - £22 adult, £12 under 16s. Sole use £700. Dogs £5/night.

CONTACT: Ben and Jenny
Tel: 01687 462163 or 01687 310324
bunkhouse@knoydart.org
knoydart.org/knoydart-bunkhouse/
Inverie, Knoydart, By Mallaig, Inverness-shire PH41 4PL

DETAILS
- **Open** - All year. All day. 9-11am & 5-10pm
- **Beds** - 39
- **Price/night** - From £23pp. ID required for check in.

CONTACT: Receptionist
Tel: 01599 534510
info@skyebackpackers.com
skyebackpackers.com/
Benmhor, Kyleakin, Skye, IV41 8PH

SKYE BASECAMP

173a

Skye Basecamp is a fabulous centrally located bunkhouse with mostly private en suite rooms. Perfect for lovers of the great outdoors, with hot showers, comfy beds and a great drying room.

Shops & bars all within walking distance. Knowledgeable staff and enthusiastic guests create a fantastic atmosphere. Join us for sunset panoramas across the shores of Broadford Bay or take a stroll to the beach with its resident otters.

DETAILS

- **Open** - All year. Check in 4-8pm.
- **Beds** - 32: 6x4 en suite, 2x4
- **Price/night** - Seasonal from £24pp. Discounts for longer stays and exclusive use.

CONTACT: Catriona Lates
Tel: 01471 820044 or 07517 196989
bookings@skyebasecamp.co.uk
www.skyebasecamp.co.uk/
Lime Park, Broadford, Isle of Skye
IV49 9AE

WATERFRONT
BUNKHOUSE

173b

Feet from the edge of Loch Harport, Isle of Skye, with breathtaking views of the Cuillins, this purpose built, stylish & comfortable bunkhouse is an ideal base for hill walkers or sightseers. There is spectacular scenery and abundant wildlife in the surrounding hills and glens. The bunkhouse has a kitchen and common room with a balcony overlooking the loch and 5 bunkrooms, one en suite. The Old Inn, a traditional highland pub provides breakfast, lunch and dinner if required.

DETAILS

- **Open** - All year. All day.
- **Beds** - 24: 2x6, 2x4, 1x4 en suite.
- **Price/night** - £30pp. En suite £35pp. Sole use £550. Booking essential.

CONTACT: Elaine
Tel: 01478 640205
enquiries@theoldinnskye.co.uk
www.theoldinnskye.co.uk
The Old Inn, Carbost, Isle of Skye,
IV47 8SR

HEB
HOSTEL
174a

The Heb Hostel is a family-run backpackers hostel in the heart of Stornoway on the enchanting Isle of Lewis. It's ideal for travellers visiting the Hebrides. Cyclists, walkers, surfers, families & groups are all welcome. Clean, comfortable, friendly & relaxed, Heb Hostel aims to provide a quality stay at budget prices. There are many facilities, including a common room with peat fire, free WiFi and local guides.

DETAILS

- **Open** - March - October. Open all day but may need to phone for access code.
- **Beds** - 30: 1x8, 2x7,1x4 (family), 2x2.
- **Price/night** - Dorm £23pp. Family room £90/£110. Twin/double from £70. Shepherds hut from £80.

CONTACT:Christine Macintosh
Tel: 01851 709889
christine@hebhostel.com
www.hebhostel.com
25 Kenneth St, Stornoway, Isle of Lewis, HS1 2DR

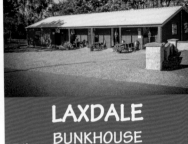

LAXDALE
BUNKHOUSE
174b

Laxdale Bunkhouse, on the Isle of Lewis, lies within Laxdale Holiday Park, a small family-run park set in peaceful leafy surroundings. Just 1.5 miles away from the town of Stornoway, it's an ideal base for exploring the island. Built in 1998, the bunkhouse has four rooms of four bunks. There is a drying room, a spacious fully equipped dining kitchen, a comfortable TV lounge and BBQ area. Toilets/showers are located in the building & are suitable for the disabled. Wigwams are also available.

DETAILS

- **Open** - March to Nov. 9am - 10pm.
- **Beds** - 16: 4x4.
- **Price/night** - £22 adult, £19 child, £75 room (3 or less people) £330 sole use.

CONTACT: Gordon Macleod
Tel: 01851 706966 or 01851 703234
info@laxdaleholidaypark.com
www.laxdaleholidaypark.com
Laxdale Holiday Park, 6 Laxdale Lane, Stornoway, Isle of Lewis, HS2 0DR

GEARRANNAN
HOSTEL & BUNKHOUSE
175a

GRINNEABHAT
HOSTEL
175b

Part of the Gearrannan Blackhouse Village on the Isle of Lewis, the Gearrannan Hostel has been refurbished to sleep 13 including a 3 bed family room. Warm and cosy it has a well equipped kitchen & two modern shower rooms. The bunkhouse (groups only) sleeps 14 in bunks. The perfect base for many local attractions from surfing to country walks, archaeology to cycling. There are also 3 holiday cottages.

DETAILS
- **Open** - All year. No arrivals on Sundays.
- **Beds** - Hostel: 13: 1x6, 1x4, 1x3. Bunkhouse: 14: 2x6 1x2. Black houses: 1x2, 2x3-5
- **Price/night** - Hostel: from £25pp, family room £85

CONTACT: Mairi
Tel: 01851 643416
info@gearrannan.com
www.gearrannan.com
5a Gearrannan Carloway Isle of Lewis
HS2 9AL

Grinneabhat is a new community owned and run hostel on the Isle of Lewis.

Sleeping 12 across 4 ensuite rooms you can book a bed, a room or the whole hostel.

Grinneabhat hostel makes the perfect base for exploring this enchanting island, it's history and culture, deserted beaches and abundant wildlife.

All bed linen and towels are provided.

Dogs are welcome by arrangement.

DETAILS
- **Open** - All year
- **Beds** - 12: 2x4, 2x2
- **Price/night** - From £30pp

CONTACT: Tina Macphail
Tel: 01851 710210
info@bragararnol.org
www.grinneabhat.com/
North Bragar, Isle of Lewis. HS2 9DA

RAVENSPOINT
HOSTEL
176a

BACKPACKERS
STOP
176b

On the unspoilt Isle of Lewis, Ravenspoint Hostel sits on the shores of Loch Erisort, providing comfortable accommodation in a traditional crofting community where Gaelic is still spoken on a daily basis.

Whether travelling by bike, car or on foot, look out for white-tailed eagles, otters, deer and enjoy exploring the community-owned Pairc Estate on which the hostel sits alongside a small shop, tea-room, fuel service and museum.

Situated in the village of Tarbert on the Isle of Harris, the Backpackers Stop is a comfortable hostel for travellers. Close to the ferry, bus, shops, cafés, bars and restaurants. The Backpackers Stop is a handy base for exploring Harris, as well as whilst walking or cycling the islands. Ideal when arriving by ferry.

Self-catering kitchen, lounge & shared dorms. Linen, duvets & towels provided. USB sockets, free WiFi. Tea & coffee available all day. Basic self service breakfast provided. Keycode entry.

DETAILS
- **Open** - 1st March - 31st October 2023
- **Beds** - 9: 1xdbl, 1xtwin, 1x5 bunks
- **Price/night** - Private double or twin room £60. Shared dorm room £24pp.

CONTACT: Ishbel
Tel: 01851 880236
hostel@ravenspoint.net
ravenspoint.net
Kershader, South Lochs, Isle of Lewis, HS2 9QA

DETAILS
- **Open** - 1st March - 10th November. All year round for large groups/private use.
- **Beds** - 19: 3 rooms
- **Price/night** - £25 per person.

CONTACT: Lee
Tel: 07708 746745
bpackers_stop@hotmail.com
www.backpackers-stop.co.uk
Main St., Tarbert, Isle of Harris, HS3 3DJ

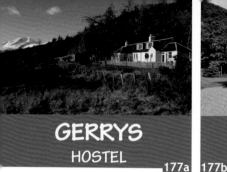

GERRYS
HOSTEL
177a

FOREST WAY
BUNKHOUSE
177b

Gerry's Hostel is a rustic cottage with a live-in host, situated in a wilderness area on the most scenic railway in Britain. It is on the Cape Wrath Trail, The T.G.O Challenge Route and is 0.5 miles from the Coulin Pass at Craig. It sleeps up to 20 in a large dormitory & family rooms, with some heating. Meals & draught ale are 15 min drive away. Great location for walking, climbing, fishing, cycling, golfing and wildlife watching.

Close to the idyllic fishing village of Ullapool in a peaceful rural setting with lots of wildlife. A perfect base for climbers & walkers with 22 Munros and many other hills in the area.

Next to Lael Forest Gardens which is renowned for its wildlife. The bunkhouse is ideally located for touring the North West Highlands with easy access to the areas of Torridon and up to Assynt.

DETAILS

- **Open** - All year. Check in after 4pm
- **Beds** - 20: 1x10, 2x5/6
- **Price/night** - From £25pp main dorm for the single night, additional nights are £20pp. Family room from £25pp (min 2 guests). Twins and doubles available .

DETAILS

- **Open** - All year.
- **Beds** - 11: 2x4, 1x3 (dbl + sgl). All en suite
- **Price/night** - £25pp, £100 per room, £180 for the whole hostel. Discounts for stays of more than 1 night (see website for more info).

CONTACT: Simon
Tel: 07894 984294 or 01520 766232
s.howkins@gmail.com
gerryshostel.com
Craig Achnashellach, Strathcarron,
Wester Ross, IV54 8YU

CONTACT: Iain
Tel: 07912 177419
bookings@forestway.co.uk
www.forestway.co.uk
Lael, Lochbroom, IV23 2RS

THE CEILIDH PLACE
BUNKHOUSE
178a

BADRALLACH
BOTHY & CAMPSITE
178b

The Ceilidh Place, in the centre of Ullapool, is a unique small complex, consisting of a music venue/performance space, restaurant, hotel, bar, bookshop, coffee shop, gallery and bunkhouse. There are regular ceilidhs, concerts & plays. The bunkhouse does not have self-catering facilities but the coffee shop is open from 8.30am to late evening all week including weekends. Rooms are also available in the hotel. The village of Ullapool is a small exciting port and fishing town, with ferries from the Outer Hebrides. Hill walkers and families especially love staying here.

On the tranquil shores of Little Loch Broom overlooking one of Scotland's finest mountain ranges, Badrallach Bothy and Campsite offer a fine base for walking or relaxing. Fish in the nearby lochs or simply enjoy the flora and fauna. Hot showers, spotless accommodation, an unbelievable price and the feeling of remoteness make the Bothy and Campsite a firm favourite. There is also a holiday cottage for hire.

DETAILS
- **Open** - All year. All day.
- **Beds** - 12: (area is for sleeping mats and bags - no beds)
- **Price/night** - £10pp, £2 per vehicle. £100 sole use. See @badrallachcampsite facebook page for camping/cottage fees.

DETAILS
- **Open** - All year.
- **Beds** - Bunkhouse: 32
- **Price/night** - Get in touch for prices.

CONTACT: Reception
Tel: 01854 612103
stay@theceilidhplace.com
www.theceilidhplace.com
14 West Argyle St. Ullapool, IV26 2TY

CONTACT: Chris Davidson
Tel: 07719 536870
mail@badrallach.com
www.badrallach.com
Croft No 9, Badrallach, Dundonnell, Ross-shire, IV23 2QP

INCHNADAMPH
LODGE

179a

Inchnadamph Lodge Assynt is a grand house tastefully converted to provide a variety of accommodation in the Scottish Highlands.

Choose from private rooms, dorms, a self-catering cottage, shepherd huts and steading studio apartments.

Located at the foot of Ben More Assynt, overlooking Loch Assynt, it is a great base to explore one of the wildest areas in the Highlands. On North Coast 500 classic road route.

DETAILS
- **Open** - Mid March to Mid Oct. All day
- **Beds** - 65
- **Price/night** - From £29pp

CONTACT: Manager
Tel: 01571 822218
hello@inchnadamph.com
www.inchnadamph.com
Inchnadamph, Assynt, Lairg, Sutherland.
IV27 4HL

STOER
HOSTEL

179b

Stoer Hostel is a warm & spacious conversion of a former church. Situated on the B869 it is near 3 gorgeous beaches & Stoer Lighthouse is 4 miles away.

A great base for exploring the stunning hills of Assynt & its spectacular coastline. The hostel sleeps 22 in 4 bunk rooms, 2 twin rooms and 1 self-contained flat. There is a drying room, utility room, huge open plan living area, wood burning stove & free WiFi. Groups welcome.

DETAILS
- **Open** - Check in: 5 - 11 pm. Check out by 10 am.
- **Beds** - 22: 2x2, 4x4 + self contained double flat
- **Price/night** - From £30 per person.

CONTACT: Claire
Tel: 01571 855388 or 07933 121729
booking@stoerhostel.co.uk
www.stoerhostel.co.uk
Lochinver, Sutherland, IV27 4JE

BUNKHOUSE
@ INVERSHIN HOTEL
180a

HELMSDALE
LODGE HOSTEL
180b

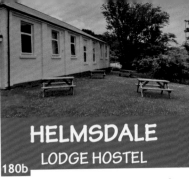

Situated within a small hotel in the north Highlands, the bunkhouse consists of 4 rooms with a shared shower room & toilet. Guests can enjoy the hotel facilities; comfortable reception area, cosy bar with real fire, real ale and regular music sessions. Cyclists, walkers, bikers, fishermen, Munro baggers, families and individuals are all welcome. The bunkhouse is just off the North Coast 500 road route. No self-catering facilities but breakfast & evening meals are available.

Set in the scenic coastal village of Helmsdale, all six rooms at the Lodge are en-suite. There is a fully equipped kitchen and comfortable lounge area with log burning stove. On the NC500 and Land's End to John O'Groats routes, the Lodge is popular with 'end to enders' and walkers exploring the far north Marilyn Hills. Perfect stopover en route to Orkney. Pets welcome on request. Groups welcome.

DETAILS

■ **Open** - All year. Advanced bookings only from Nov-March - contact manager.
■ **Beds** - 24: 6x4 (all private en-suite)
■ **Price/night** - Adults from £28. Children from £15. Dog £10 per stay. Private en suite from £70.

DETAILS

■ **Open** - April-end Sept. Check in 4pm.
■ **Beds** - 10: 2x twin, 2x triple (bunkbeds)
■ **Price/night** - From £25pp. Breakfast optional extra.

CONTACT: Angus or Cheryl
Tel: 01549 421202
enquiries@invershin.com
www.invershin.com
Invershin Hotel, Lairg
Sutherland, IV27 4ET

CONTACT: Marie
Tel: 07971 922356 or 07971 516287
stay@helmsdalehostel.co.uk
www.helmsdalehostel.co.uk
Stafford Street, Helmsdale
Sutherland, KW8 6JR

CORNMILL
BUNKHOUSE
181a

KYLE OF TONGUE
HOSTEL & CAMPSITE
181b

Cornmill Bunkhouse is situated on a traditional croft. The mill was built in the early 1800s and was active until 1920s. It is now 4* accommodation for individuals or groups. Guests are reminded of their historic setting; the smaller bunkroom has a patio door looking onto the workings of the old mill with its large wooden cog driving wheels. Activities can be organised for groups including laser tagging & shooting. Hen and stag parties welcome.

The Kyle of Tongue Hostel & Campsite is a stone lodge & campsite, situated on the shores of a sea loch on the Scottish North Coast. Furnished, like a boutique hotel, but with all the friendliness of a hostel. There are comfortable private bedrooms, a relaxing cafe bar, a lounge/dining room and a well stocked shop. The campsite is fully equipped and has panoramic views of Castle Varich, Ben Hope & Ben Loyal. Holiday cottage and static caravan are also available.

DETAILS

- **Open** - All year. Advanced notice required 1st Oct - 1st April. All day.
- **Beds** - 14: 1x8,1x6
- **Price/night** - £25pp. Discounts available for group bookings.

CONTACT: Sandy Murray
Tel: 01641 571219 or 07808 197350
sandy.murray2@btinternet.com
www.cornmillbunkhouse.co.uk
Cornmill Bunkhouse, Achumore, Strathhalladale, Sutherland, KW13 6YT

DETAILS

- **Open** - April to October. Check in from 2pm
- **Beds** - 20 in hostel, plus cottage, static caravan and a large campsite.
- **Price/night** - From £25. Private rooms from £60. Contact for other prices.

CONTACT: Carol Mackay
Tel: 01847 611789
kothostelandhp@btinternet.com
www.tonguehostelandholidaypark.co.uk
Tongue, By Lairg, Sutherland, IV27 4XH

SANDRAS
HOSTEL
182a

182b

BROWNS
HOSTEL & HOUSES

Thurso is the northern-most town on the UK mainland. The cliffs are alive with guillemots, kittiwakes, fulmars & puffins, while the sea is home to seals & porpoises. The 4* hostel has en suites in all rooms, (some have TVs). Using their own backpacking experience, the owners ensure you will enjoy a level of comfort and service second to none. Surfing, pony trekking, fishing, quad biking, coastal walks and boat trips are all available nearby. On the NC500 route.

Providing nightly and weekly self-catering accommodation in the captivating small town of Stromness, Orkney. Within walking/cycling distance of the ancient Maeshowe, Ring of Brodgar and Skara Brae. Stromness has a museum, art centre, festivals, scuba diving, sea angling etc. Facilities include fully equipped kitchens, single, double, twin, triple and family bedrooms, some with sinks and others with ensuite. All with towels and bedding inclusive. WiFi. Cycle storage & free car park up the lane.

DETAILS

- **Open** - All year
- **Beds** - 26: 1x6, 2x4, 1x3, 4x2
- **Price/night** - Dorm £22pp. Double/twin £50. Family room £80 (4 people), £95 (5 people). Breakfast is included in the price.

CONTACT: George or James
Tel: 01847 894575
info@sandras-backpackers.co.uk
sandras-backpackers.co.uk
24-26 Princes Street, Thurso, Caithness, KW14 7BQ

DETAILS

- **Open** - All year. All day. No curfew.
- **Beds** - 28: 3x1, 4x2, 3x3, 2x4
- **Price/night** - From £23pp.

CONTACT: Sylvia Brown
Tel: 01856 850661
info@brownsorkney.co.uk
www.brownsorkney.co.uk
45/47 Victoria Street, Stromness, Orkney, KW16 3BS

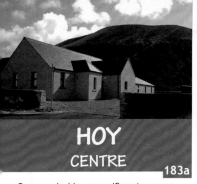

HOY
CENTRE

183a

RACKWICK
HOSTEL

183b

Surrounded by magnificent scenery, the Hoy Centre is perfect a peaceful & relaxing holiday. It's also an ideal venue for walking, outdoor education, weddings, workshops, clubs or family gatherings. Offering high quality, 4* accommodation, the centre has a well-equipped kitchen, comfortable lounge & a large dining hall. All rooms are en suite with twin beds and one set of bunks. Hoy is an RSPB reserve comprising 3,500ha of upland heath & cliffs with a large variety of wildlife including arctic hares.

In the scenic Rackwick Valley in the north of Hoy, the 3* hostel overlooks Rackwick Bay considered one of the most beautiful places in Orkney. It sleeps 8 across 2 rooms of 4 beds. There's a small kitchen with a good range of utensils and a separate dining area. Singles, families and groups are welcome for private room or whole hostel bookings. Car parking and bike storage behind the hostel. Walkers and Cyclists Welcome.

DETAILS

- **Open** - All year.
- **Beds** - 32
- **Price/night** - Please phone for prices for singles, families or groups.

DETAILS

- **Open** - All year.
- **Beds** - 8: 2x4
- **Price/night** - For prices please check accommodation's website or phone.

CONTACT: Customer Services
Tel: 01856 873535 ext 2901
stromnesscs@orkney.gov.uk
www.orkney.gov.uk/Service-Directory/S/
hoy-centre.htm
Hoy, Orkney, KW16 3NJ

CONTACT: Customer Services
Tel: 01856 850907 or 01856 873535 ext 2901
stromnesscs@orkney.gov.uk
www.orkney.gov.uk/Service-Directory/S/
rackwick-outdoor-centre.htm
Rackwick Hostel, Rackwick, Hoy,
Orkney, KW16 3NJ

BIRSAY
HOSTEL
184a

OBSERVATORY
HOSTEL
184b

Birsay Hostel in the northwest corner of the Orkney mainland offers comfortable accommodation for groups of 10 to 26 in 5 bedrooms. An ideal venue for outdoor education trips, clubs or family gatherings. It has a well equipped kitchen, dining area, drying room, disabled access and all bed linen is provided. There is a campsite in the extensive grounds. Close to spectacular coast, RSPB reserves, early settlements and UNESCO heritage sites.

On a 34 acre croft managed by the North Ronaldsay Bird Observatory on the most northern isle of Orkney. Adjacent to a shell sand beach visited by seals and unique seaweed-eating sheep. Spectacular bird migrations and outstanding views. Ideal accommodation for those interested in wildlife but welcomes all. The hostel sleeps 10 in three dormitories with a self-catering kitchen. Lounge bar and meals available in the Observatory Guest House.

DETAILS

■ **Open** - April to September. Out of season booking may be available by arrangement for large bookings.
■ **Beds** - 26: 2x4,1x2,1x6,1x10 + camping.
■ **Price/night** - Prices on enquiry.

CONTACT: Customer Services
Tel: 01856 850907 or 01856 873535 ext 2901
stromnesscs@orkney.gov.uk
www.orkney.gov.uk
Birsay, Orkney, KW17 2LY

DETAILS

■ **Open** - All year. All day. No curfews.
■ **Beds** - 10: 2x4,1x2 + Guest house.
■ **Price/night** - Hostel: £20.50 - £21, half board from £43.50. Guest house: private rooms £62 - £85 half board.

CONTACT: Duty Warden
Tel: 01857 633200
enquiries@nrbo.org.uk
www.nrbo.org.uk/accommodation
NRBO, North Ronaldsay,
Orkney Islands, KW17 2BE

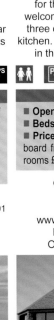

AYRES ROCK
HOSTEL

Sanday is the perfect place to take time out, with long stretches of unspoilt sandy beaches, an abundance of birds, seals and other wildlife, glittering seas, clear air and spectacular skies.

Those lucky enough to live here enjoy a rare quality of life in a small, friendly and safe community.

Credited 4 Stars VisitScotland

DETAILS
- **Open** - All year. 8am to 10pm.
- **Beds** - 8 : 2x2 (twin), 1x4 (en suite). Pods: 3x2 + campsite
- **Price/night** - Single room £30. Twin room from £40. Groups up to 8 from £60. Camping pods from £25. Twin pod £35.

CONTACT: Julie or Paul
Tel: 01857 600410
sandayhostel@gmail.com
www.ayres-rock-hostel-orkney.com
Ayre, Coo Road, Sanday
Orkney KW17 2AY

GARDIESFAULD
HOSTEL

Gardiesfauld Hostel is on Unst, the most northerly of the Shetland Isles with spectacular cliffs sculpted by the Atlantic Ocean on the west and secluded, sandy beaches on the east with rocky outcrops where seals and otters appear.

On the picturesque shore at Uyeasound, this refurbished hostel has good facilities and a relaxed atmosphere. There is a kitchen, dining room, lounge, conservatory and rooms with en suite facilities as well as a garden when you can pitch a tent or park your caravan.

DETAILS
- **Open** - April to October. Open in winter for pre-bookings. Open all day.
- **Beds** - 35: 1x11, 2x6, 2x5, 1x2
- **Price/night** - Adults £16, U16's £9. Camping £8, U16s £4. Hook ups £18

CONTACT: Warden
Tel: 01957 755279
enquiries@gardiesfauld.shetland.co.uk
Uyeasound, Unst, Shetland, ZE2 9DW

NEED HELP FINDING THAT PERFECT PLACE?
GO TO OUR WEBSITE

Independenthostels.co.uk

Search for:

hostels in your chosen location

hostels available on your chosen dates

hostels along your next long distance route

hostels ideal & available for your group

You will find:

great maps

lots more information and photos

inspirational articles and holiday ideas

last minute deals

online booking at the lowest prices

INDEX

INDEX